Yide Ma
Kun Zhan
Zhaobin Wang

Applications of Pulse-Coupled Neural Networks

Yide Ma
Kun Zhan
Zhaobin Wang

Applications of Pulse-Coupled Neural Networks

With 161 Figures

高等教育出版社
HIGHER EDUCATION PRESS

Springer

Authors
Yide Ma
School of Information Science and Engineering
Lanzhou University
Gansu 730000, P. R. China
E-mail: ydma@lzu.edu.cn

Kun Zhan
School of Information Science and Engineering
Lanzhou University
Gansu 730000, P. R. China
E-mail: ice.echo@gmail.com

Zhaobin Wang
School of Information Science and Engineering
Lanzhou University
Gansu 730000, P. R. China
E-mail: wangzhaobin@126.com

ISBN 978-7-04-027978-8
Higher Education Press, Beijing

ISBN 978-3-642-13744-0 ISBN 978-3-642-13745-7 (eBook)
Springer Heidelberg Dordrecht London New York

Library of Congress Control Number: 2010928904

Cover design: Frido Steinen-Broo, EStudio Calamar, Spain

Printed on acid-free paper

Springer is part of Springer Science + Business Media (www.springer.com)

Preface

There is no more complicated, advantaged and powerful device than the mammalian primate cortical visual system for image processing in nature. The pulse-coupled neural network (PCNN) is inspired from the investigation of pulse synchronization within the mammalian visual cortex, and has been widely applied to image processing and pattern recognition.

Visual cortex is the passage for brain to acquire information from eyes and a part of brain central nervous system. Several biological models based on visual cortex were proposed through investigation of cat cortex and had been applied to image processing.

The PCNN emulates the mammalian visual cortex, which is supposed to be one of the most efficient image processing methods. The output of the PCNN is a series of pulse images which represent the fundamental features of original stimulus, such as edge, texture, and segment. Neurons receive inputs from other neurons through synapses and are fired synchronously in certain regions, that is why the PCNN can be applied to image segmentation, smoothing, and coding. Another important feature of the PCNN is that the pulse images are able to be characterized to a unique invariant signature for the image retrieval.

This book analyzes the PCNN in detail and presents some special applications and corresponding results based on our own researches.

Contributions of the book have come from Hongjuan Zhang, Rongchang Zhao, Maojun Su, Dongmei Lin, Xiaojun Li, Guanzhu Xu, Xin Wang, Zaifeng Zhang, Xiaowen Feng, Haibo Deng, Li Liu, Xiaozhe Xu, Chunliang Qi, Chenghu Wu, Fei Shi, Zhibai Qian, Qing Liu, Min Yuan, Jiuwen Zhang, Yingjie Liu, Xiaolei Chen, and our graduate students at Circuit and System Research Institute of Lanzhou University.

This work was supported by the National Natural Science Foundation of China under the No.60872109, Program for New Century Excellent Talents in University under the No.NCET-06-0900, National Natural Science Foundation in Gansu Province under the No.0710RJZA015, and the Subproject of 985-3rd for Lanzhou University.

We would like to give many thanks to Ms. Hongying Chen for her excellent support, help, and suggestion for the publication of this book.

Yide Ma, Kun Zhan, Zhaobin Wang
14 May 2010

Contents

Chapter 1 Pulse-Coupled Neural Networks

The image captured by eyes is transmitted to brain by the optic nerve, and the image signal is transferred in the fiber pathways and finally processed by the primate visual cortex dominantly. The primate visual cortex is devoted to visual processing, and nearly all visual signals reach the cortex via the primary visual cortex. The primary visual cortex is the largest and most important visual cortical area, and does so when neurons in the cortex fire action potentials as stimuli appear within their receptive fields. Signal produced in neurons is transferred to their neighbors by means of localized contact of synapses, which are located on the dendrites and also on the neuron cell body. Electrical charges produced at the synapses propagate to the soma and produce a net postsynaptic potential. If the postsynaptic potential is large enough to exceed a threshold value, the neuron generates an action potential. Synchronized Gama oscillations ($30-100$ Hz) were found in the primary visual cortex of mammalian [1, 2]. In Ref. [2], the linking field model was proposed based on the hypothesis that neuronal pulse synchronizations can be partitioned into two types: stimulus-forced and stimulus-induced synchronizations. Stimulus-forced synchronizations are directly driven by stimulus transients and establish fast but crude sketches of association in the visual cortex, while stimulus-induced synchronizations are believed to be produced via process among local neural oscillations that are mutually connected. The feeding and the linking create the membrane potential. A single feeding input of a neuron is connected to a spatially corresponding stimulus, and the linking inputs of each neuron are connected to the output of the neighboring neurons within the same predetermined radius. Based on the studies of the linking field model, the pulse-coupled neural network (PCNN) were developed and applied to image processing and pattern recognition [3, 4].

1.1 Linking Field Model

The fundamental components of the model [2] are different leaky integrators shown in Fig. 1.1. A leaky integrator is realized as first-order recursive digital filter. The impulse response of a leaky integrator is

$$I(t) = V_x \exp(-t/\tau_x), \tag{1.1}$$

where x denotes certain leaky integrator; V_x is the amplification factor; and τ_x is the decay time constant. For certain V_x and τ_x, $I(t)$ is of exponential decay with time t.

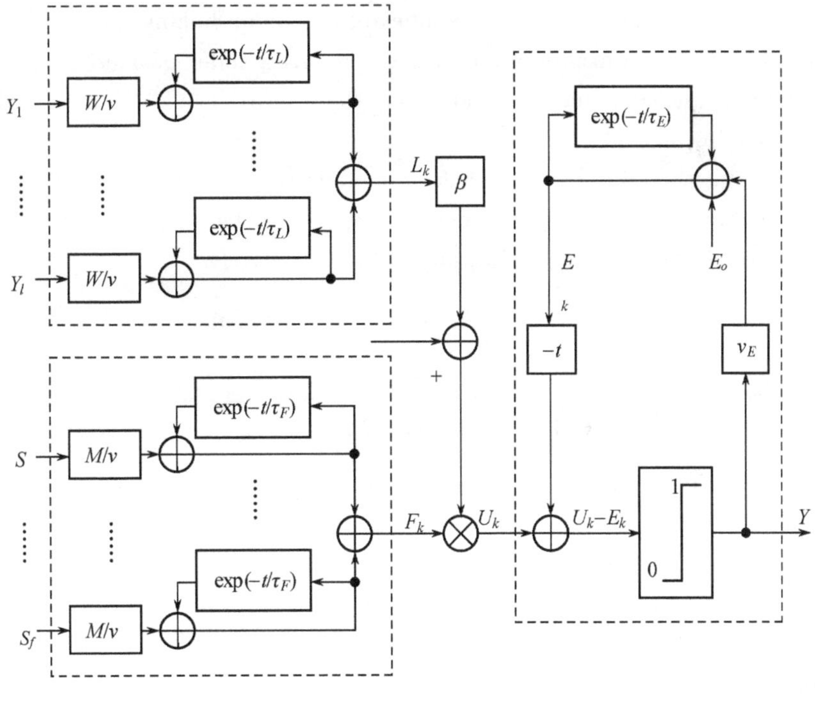

Fig. 1.1. Linking Field Model

The feeding F and linking L are combined together as neuron's internal activity U. Neuron receives input signals via feeding synapse M, and each neuron is connected to its neighbors such that its output signal modulates the activity of its neighbors via linking synapses L.

$$\begin{cases} F_{jk}[n] = F_{jk}[n-1]\exp(-t/\tau_F) + V_F S_j[n] M_{jk}, \\ F_k[n] = \sum_{j=1}^{f} F_{jk}[n]; \end{cases} \tag{1.2}$$

$$\begin{cases} L_{ik}[n] = L_{ik}[n-1]\exp(-t/\tau_L) + V_L Y_i[n-1] M_{ik}, \\ L_k[n] = \sum_{i=1}^{l} L_{ik}[n]; \end{cases} \tag{1.3}$$

$$U_k[n] = F_k[n](1 + \beta L_k[n]); \tag{1.4}$$

where n is the time index; i is the index of neuron on linking input; j is the index of neuron on feeding input; k is the counting index of neuron; τ_F and τ_L are the time constants; V_F and V_L are the magnitude adjustments; and β is the linking strength of the PCNN.

The pulse is able to feed back to modulate the threshold, raising the threshold by magnitude V_E that decreases with τ_E. The threshold and output are generally given by Eqs. (1.5) and (1.6), respectively.

$$E_k[n] = E_k[n-1]\exp(-t/\tau_E) + V_E Y_k[n-1]; \tag{1.5}$$

$$Y_k[n] = \begin{cases} 1 & U_k[n] > E_k[n], \\ 0 & \text{Otherwise.} \end{cases} \tag{1.6}$$

If U is the physical intensity of a stimulus, then it is a constant C for a single neuron. Putting $U = C = E$ into Eq. (1.5), then the time when the pulses occur can be computed by

$$t = \tau_E \ln(V_E/C) + m\tau_E \ln(1 + V_E/C), \quad m = 0, 1, \ldots . \tag{1.7}$$

Thus neuron's firing frequency is

$$f = \frac{1}{\tau_E \ln(1 + V_E/C)}. \tag{1.8}$$

1.2 PCNN

As shown in Fig. 1.2, the PCNN neuron accepts the feeding input F and the linking input L and then generates the internal activity U. When U is greater than the dynamic threshold E, the PCNN produces sequential pulse sequence Y.

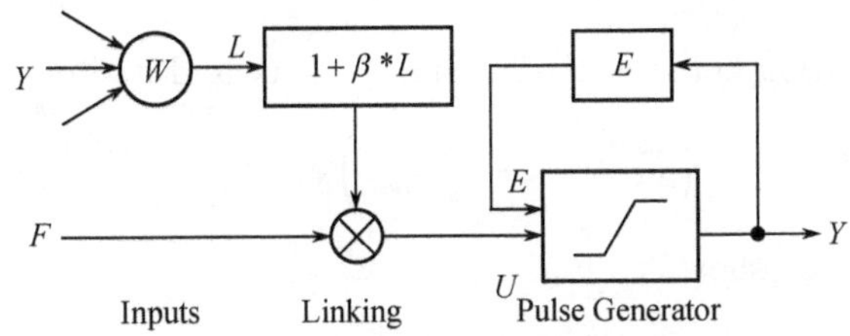

Fig. 1.2. The basic PCNN neuron

For the convenience of simulation, the PCNN is modified [3, 4]. Its model is as follows:

$$F_{ij}[n] = \mathrm{e}^{-\alpha_F} F_{ij}[n-1] + V_F \sum_{kl} M_{ijkl} Y_{kl}[n-1] + S_{ij}; \tag{1.11}$$

$$L_{ij}[n] = \mathrm{e}^{-\alpha_L} L_{ij}[n-1] + V_L \sum_{kl} W_{ijkl} Y_{kl}[n-1]; \tag{1.12}$$

$$U_{ij}[n] = F_{ij}[n](1 + \beta L_{ij}[n]); \tag{1.13}$$

$$E_{ij}[n] = E_{ij}[n-1]\mathrm{e}^{-\alpha_E} + V_E Y_{ij}[n-1]; \tag{1.14}$$

$$Y_{ij}[n] = \begin{cases} 1 & U_{ij}[n] > E_{ij}[n], \\ 0 & \text{Otherwise}. \end{cases} \tag{1.15}$$

where α_F, α_L, and α_E are the time constants; V_F, V_L, and V_E are the magnitude adjustments; β is the linking strength of the PCNN.

Each neuron is denoted with indices (i, j), and one of its neighboring neurons is denoted with indices (k, l). Feeding F is combined with linking L as neuron's internal activity U. The neuron receives input signals via feeding synapse M, and each neuron is connected to its neighbors such that the output signal of a neuron modulates the activity of its neighbors via linking synapse W. The pulse is able to feed back to modulate the threshold E via a leaky integrator, raising the threshold by magnitude V_E that decreases with time constant α_E. During iterations when a neuron's internal activity U exceeds its dynamic threshold E, pulse is generated.

In order to analyze single neuron's firing periodicity, we suppose that there is no coupled stimulus induced, and then the internal activity would be described by

$$U_{ij}[n] = e^{-\alpha_F} F_{ij}[n-1] + S_{ij} = F_{ij}[0]e^{-n\alpha_F} + \frac{1-e^{-n\alpha_F}}{1-e^{-\alpha_F}} S_{ij}. \tag{1.16}$$

Notice the relation between the internal activity and its iteration time n,

$$U_{ij}[n] = \left(F_{ij}[0] - \frac{S_{ij}}{1-e^{-\alpha_F}} \right) e^{-n\alpha_F} + \frac{S_{ij}}{1-e^{-\alpha_F}}. \tag{1.17}$$

Eq. (1.16) can be shown as Fig. 1.3.

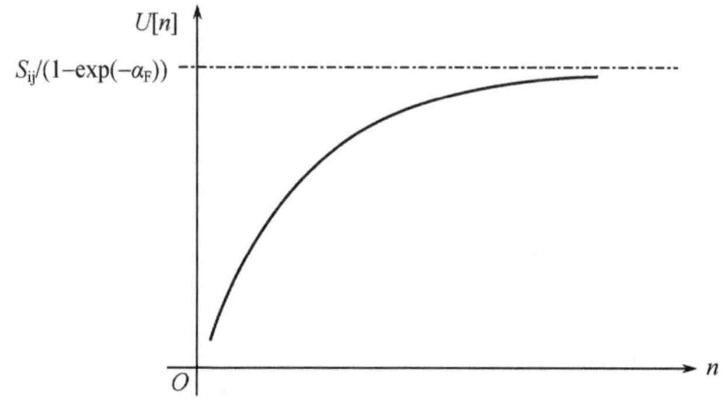

Fig. 1.3. The schematic representation of internal activity without stimulus induced

The static threshold can be described by

$$E_{ij}[n] = E_{ij}[0]e^{-n\alpha_E}. \tag{1.18}$$

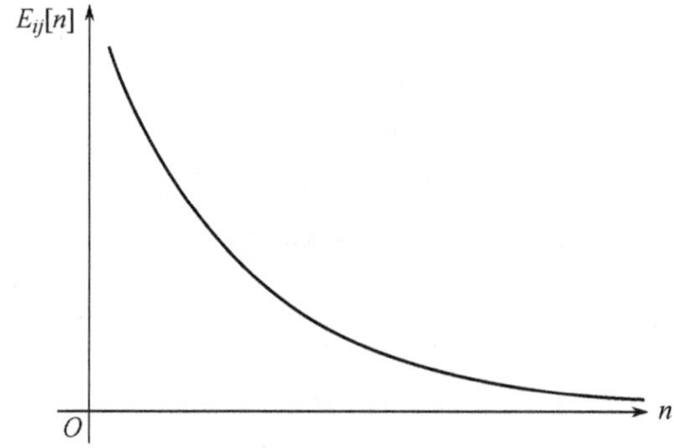

Fig. 1.4. The schematic representation of dynamic threshold while no pulse occurs

Therefore, the internal activity of neuron is compared with the dynamic threshold to decide whether to produce output pulse or not. Combining Fig.

1.3 with Fig. 1.4 we can obtain the pulse output of the PCNN as shown in Fig. 1.5.

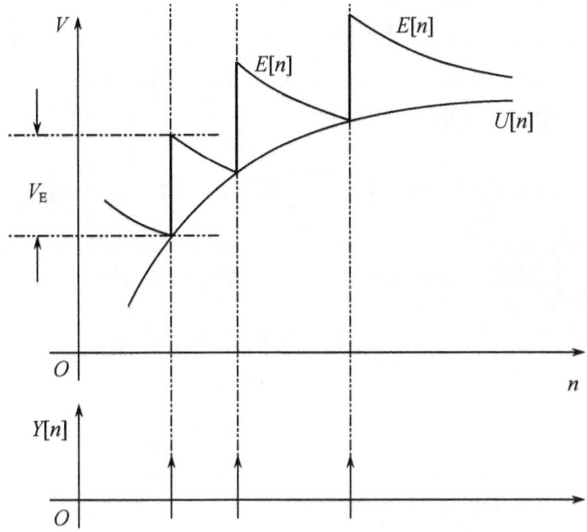

Fig. 1.5. The schematic representation of output of the PCNN without stimulus induced

So the $(k+1)$ times pulse occurs at the iteration number n_k:

$$n_k = \frac{1}{\alpha_E} \ln\left(\frac{E[0]}{U[n_1]}\right) + \sum_k \frac{1}{\alpha_E} \ln\left(\frac{U[n_{k-1}] + V_E}{U[n_k]}\right). \tag{1.19}$$

If the internal activity is equal to its stimulus when neuron receives a constant in the network, from Eq. (1.19) we can obtain the firing frequency of PCNN as follows:

$$f_{ij} = \frac{\alpha_E}{\ln(1 + V_E/S_{ij})}. \tag{1.20}$$

1.3 Modified PCNN

Three modified models are introduced in this section. They are the intersection cortical mode, the spiking cortical model, and the multi-channel PCNN, respectively.

1.3.1 Intersection Cortical Model

The Intersection Cortical Model (ICM) is a simplified model of the PCNN [5]. The ICM is a special case of the PCNN when there are no linking neurons. The ICM is only with feeding inputs, and if the linking strength of the PCNN is set to 0's, it will become the ICM.

$$F_{ij}[n] = fF_{ij}[n-1] + \sum_{kl} M_{ijkl}Y_{kl}[n-1] + S_{ij}; \tag{1.21}$$

$$E_{ij}[n] = gE_{ij}[n-1] + hY_{ij}[n-1]; \tag{1.22}$$

$$Y_{ij}[n] = \begin{cases} 1 & F_{ij}[n] > E_{ij}[n], \\ 0 & \text{Otherwise.} \end{cases} \tag{1.23}$$

1.3.2 Spiking Cortical Model

Neuron receives input signals via feeding synapses, and each neuron is connected to its neighbors such that the output signal of a neuron modulates the activity of its neighbors via linking synapses. Therefore, the Spiking Cortical Model [6] is given by

$$U_{ij}[n] = fU_{ij}[n-1] + S_{ij} \sum_{kl} W_{ijkl}Y_{kl}[n-1] + S_{ij}; \tag{1.24}$$

$$E_{ij}[n] = gE_{ij}[n-1] + hY_{ij}[n-1]; \tag{1.25}$$

$$Y_{ij}[n] = \begin{cases} 1 & 1/(1+\exp(-\gamma(U_{ij}[n] - E_{ij}[n]))) > 0.5, \\ 0 & \text{Otherwise.} \end{cases} \tag{1.26}$$

1.3.3 Multi-channel PCNN

As mentioned above, there is only one stimulus for each neuron. However, sometimes it cannot meet the demands in practical applications. Hence multi-stimuli are needed for one neuron. In this case, the multi-channel PCNN (m-PCNN) [7, 8] is introduced. Compared with the original model, the m-PCNN can adjust the number of external input channels according to practical demands. In the m-PCNN there are m input channels; generally, $m > 1$. All of the stimuli can be input into the model at the same time. The following expressions mathematically describe its model.

$$H_{ij}^k[n] = f^k(Y[n-1]) + S_{ij}^k; \tag{1.27}$$

$$U_{ij}[n] = \prod_{k=2}^{K}(1+\beta^k H_{ij}^k[n]) + \sigma; \tag{1.28}$$

$$Y_{ij}[n] = \begin{cases} 1 & U_{ij}[n] > E_{ij}[n-1], \\ 0 & \text{Otherwise}; \end{cases} \tag{1.29}$$

$$E_{ij}[n] = \exp(-\alpha_E)E_{ij}[n-1] + V_E Y_{ij}[n]. \tag{1.30}$$

In these equations, H^k refers to the channel of the kth external input, $S^k, k = 2, 3, ..., K$ (presume K is the total number of external inputs) and $f^k(\cdot)$ is the feed function, which shows the influence of surrounding neurons on the current neuron. β^krefers to the weighting factor of the kth channel; usually, $0 < \beta^k$ <1. The value of β^k indicates the importance of the kth channel. If one source image plays a more important role in a system than the others, its corresponding value of β^k can be increased to stress its importance. If all the inputs have parallel importance, the factors usually will be set to the same constant. σ is the level factor to adjust the average level of internal activity. Other parameters are the same as parameters in the above PCNN.

In fact, since the presentation of the PCNN many modified models besides above three models have been proposed for various purposes. For instance, the unit-linking PCNN is proposed for image shadow removal [9]. The tristate cascading PCNN is proposed for dealing with the problem of finding the shortest path [10]. The competitive PCNN is proposed to solve the problem of the shortest path tree of the network routing graph [11]. The multi-layer parallel PCNN is proposed for motion detection [12].

Summary

The PCNN is inspired from physiological studies on neuronal pulse synchronizations. It is suitable for the image processing, such as image smoothing, image binary segmentation, and feature extraction. The outputs of the PCNN are a series of pulse images, which contain plenty of information of the original image such as edge, segment, and texture feature. Hence, the pulse images can be regarded as sub-band of the original image. Based on the introduction of visual cortex, an important model-linking field model is firstly described in this chapter. And then the PCNN and its dynamic behaviors are also presented in detail. At last, some useful improved models are introduced briefly. These models will be used in the subsequent chapters.

Reference

[1] Gray CM, Konig P, Engel AK et al (1989) Oscillatory responses in cat visual cortex exhibit inter-columnar synchronization which reflects global stimulus properties. Nature 338(6213): 334 – 337

[2] Eckhorn R, Reitboeck HJ, Arndt M et al (1990) Feature linking via synchronization among distributed assemblies: simulation of results from cat cortex. Neural Computation 2(3): 293 – 307

[3] Johnson JL (1994) Pulse-coupled neural nets: translation, rotation, scale, distortion, and intensity signal invariance for images. Applied Optics 33(26): 6239 – 6253

[4] Johnson JL, Padgett ML (1999) PCNN models and applications. IEEE Transactions on Neural Networks 10(3): 480 – 498

[5] Ekblad U, Kinser JM, Atmer J et al (2004) The intersecting cortical model in image processing. Nuclear instruments and methods in physics research 525(1): 392 – 396

[6] Zhan K, Zhang HJ, Ma YD (2009) New spiking cortical model for invariant texture retrieval. IEEE Transactions on Neural Networks 20(12): 1980 – 1986

[7] Wang ZB, Ma YD (2008) Medical image fusion using m-PCNN. Information Fusion 9(2): 176 – 185

[8] Wang ZB, Ma YD (2007) Dual-channel PCNN and its application in the field of image fusion. In: The 3rd International Conference on Natural Computation, Haikou, 24 – 27 August 2007

[9] Gu XD, Yu DH, Zhang LM (2005) Image shadow removal using pulse coupled neural network. IEEE Transactions on Neural Network 16(3): 692 – 698

[10] Zhao RC, Ma YD, Zhan K (2009) Tri-state cascading pulse coupled neural network and its application in finding shortest path. Neural network world 19(6): 711 – 723

[11] Zhou DM, Nie RC, Zhao DF (2009) Analysis of autowave characteristics for competitive pulse coupled neural network and its application. Neurocomputing 72(10 – 12): 2331 – 2336

[12] Chen J, Ishimura K, WADAA M (2008) new PCNN model for motion detection. Complexity International 12: 1 – 7

Chapter 2 Image Filtering

Image filtering is able to enhance (or otherwise modify, warp, and mutilate) images and create a new image as a result of processing the pixels of an existing image. Each of pixels in the output image is computed as a function of one or several pixels in the input image, usually located near the output pixel. Different kinds of functions produce different results, and are usually used to remove different noise.

If an image is degraded by impulse noise(refer to the salt and pepper noise), only some of its pixels are changed and their gray values always tend to be extremely high or low, having low correlativity with their surrounding pixels, and obviously distinguished from those of their neighboring pixels. As another main noise existing in digital images, Gaussian noise, a stationary ergodic stochastic process, is more complex and more common. If an image is contaminated by Gaussian noise, all its pixels would be changed, which makes it very difficult to remove the noise. In this chapter, for the two types of common noise existing in images, several filtering algorithms are described and discussed respectively.

2.1 Traditional Filters

According to the relation between the input and output, that is, whether the output is a linear function of the input, tradition filters can generally be classified into two kinds: linear filter and nonlinear filter. The linear filter mainly refers to the local average filter, i.e. mean filter; while the nonlinear filter includes median filter, morphological filter, etc. In this section, we discuss them briefly.

2.1.1 Mean Filter

The mean filter smoothes input image, and works as low-pass one. Its basic idea is, for any element of the image, averaging the pixel values surrounding it. Let S_{ij} denote the set of coordinates in a rectangular window of size $m \times n$, centered at point (i, j) of the noised image $g(x, y)$. The average value of $g(x, y)$ in the area S_{ij} is defined as the value of filtered image $f'(x, y)$ at point (i, j), that is

$$f'(i,j) = \frac{1}{mn} \sum_{(x,y)\in S_{ij}} g(x,y). \tag{2.1}$$

A convolution mask with all the coefficients $1/mn$ can be used to carry out this operation.

2.1.2 Median Filter

Median filter suppresses isolated noise without blurring sharp edges. When performing median filtering, each pixel is determined by the median value of all pixels in a selected neighborhood (mask, template, and window):

$$f'(i,j) = \underset{(x,y)\in S_{ij}}{median}\{g(x,y)\}. \tag{2.2}$$

The median value $f'(i, j)$ in a window S_{ij} is that the value in which a half of the pixels have smaller values than $f'(i, j)$, and the other half have larger values than $f'(i, j)$. So the value of $f'(i, j)$ is included in the original image.

2.1.3 Morphological Filter

All morphological filters are based on two operations — dilation and erosion. They are defined in the following way:

Grayscale dilation is defined as the maximal sum of a local region of an image and a grayscale mask. The shape of the input mask (known as the structuring element, or SE) is generally chosen to emphasize or de-emphasize elements in the image. It is used to smooth small dark regions.

The general effects of performing dilation on a grayscale image are as follows:

(1) If all the values in the structuring element are positive, the output image tends to be brighter than the input.

(2) Dark elements within the image are reduced or eliminated, depending on how their shapes relate to the structuring element used.

The degree of these effects depends greatly on the shape and values within the structuring element and the details within the image itself.

Grayscale erosion is defined as the minimum of the difference of a local region of an image and a grayscale mask. The shape of the input mask (known as the structuring element, SE) is generally chosen to emphasize or de-emphasize elements in the image. It is used to smooth small light regions.

The general effects of performing erosion on a grayscale image are as follows:

(1) If all the values in the structuring element are positive, the output image tends to be darker than the input.

(2) Light elements within the image are reduced or eliminated, depending on how their shapes relate to the structuring element used.

The degree of these effects depends greatly on the shape and values within the structuring element and the details within the image itself.

Grayscale morphological opening of an image is defined as the dilation of the erosion of the image. The result is the reduction of small positive regions within the image. Grayscale morphological closing of an image is defined as the erosion of the dilation of the image. The result is the reduction of small negative regions within the image.

2.1.4 Wiener Filter [1]

Wiener filter is also called the minimum mean square filter. It incorporates both the degradation function and statistical characteristics of noise, based on random processes, and aims at finding an estimate $f'(x, y)$ of the original image $f(x, y)$ such that their mean square error is minimized. It is based on the assumption that the noise is independent of the image and with zero mean; and that gray-levels estimated are a linear function of the noisy image levels. Then the minimum of the mean square error function in the frequency domain can be expressed as follows:

$$\begin{aligned}\hat{F}(u,v) &= \left[\frac{H^*(u,v)S_f(u,v)}{S_f(u,v)\left|H(u,v)\right|^2 + S_\eta(u,v)}\right]G(u,v)\\ &= \left[\frac{H^*(u,v)}{\left|H(u,v)\right|^2 + S_\eta(u,v)/S_f(u,v)}\right]G(u,v)\\ &= \left[\frac{1}{H(u,v)}\frac{\left|H(u,v)\right|^2}{\left|H(u,v)\right|^2 + S_\eta(u,v)/S_f(u,v)}\right]G(u,v),\end{aligned} \tag{2.3}$$

where, $H(u,v)$ is the degradation function; $G(u,v)$ is the Fourier Transform of the noised image $g(x,y)$; $H^*(u,v)$ is the complex conjugate of $H(u,v)$; $|H(u,v)|^2$ is equal to $H^*(u,v)H(u,v)$; $S_\eta(u,v)$, the power spectrum of the noise, is equal to $|N(u,v)|^2$; and $S_f(u,v)$, the power spectrum of the original image, is equal to $|F(u,v)|^2$. In Eq. (2.3), the term inside the brackets is commonly referred to as the minimum mean square error filter or the least square error filter. Usually, the $S_f(u,v)$ is not known and the $S_\eta(u,v)$ is a constant for spectrally white noise, so Eq. (2.3) can be approximated to Eq. (2.4):

$$\hat{F}(u,v) = \left[\frac{1}{H(u,v)}\frac{\left|H(u,v)\right|^2}{\left|H(u,v)\right|^2 + K}\right]G(u,v), \tag{2.4}$$

where K is a specified constant determined interactively to achieve the best performance.

2.2 Impulse Noise Filtering

The filtering methods usually include two steps: noise detection and subsequent noise removal process. In this subsection, several methods based on the PCNNs, referring to the PCNN, ICM, and SCM, are discussed and analyzed.

According to the property of impulse noise, the detection of noisy pixels can be accomplished with the synchronizing pulse burst of the PCNNs. That is, in the PCNNs the noisy pixels output pulses either earlier or later. So we need only to label the coordinates of the earlier fired pixels of the input image and its inverse one. Then a certain subsequent processing is used to modify the gray values of the detected noisy pixels. Thus, image details and edges can be preserved better.

There are several subsequent noise removal methods [2−8]. Ref. [2] mentioned that the subsequent noise removal process was to modify the intensity of the detected noisy pixels step by step until the noisy pixels were activated simultaneously with the pixels around them (called Algorithm I), and in Refs. [3 – 6] the other subsequent processing methods using smoothing filters (called Algorithm II) were described.

2.2.1 Description of Algorithm I

Because of the significant intensity difference existing between the noised pixel and the pixels around it, in the PCNNs, they cannot fire simultaneously. According to the firing patterns of neurons one can modify the gray values of the detected noisy pixels like this: a pixel fires earlier than its neighbors, that is, its gray level is higher than that of its neighbors, then its gray value will be decreased step by step; while a pixel fires later than its neighbors, that is, its gray level is lower than that of its neighbors, then its gray value will be increased step by step, until the pixel fires at the same time with its neighbors. In this process, the image is really smoothed. The flow chart is shown in Fig. 2.1(a).

2.2.2 Description of Algorithm II

There is always the certain correlation between pixels in digital images. Pixels with spatial proximity tend to have similar gray value. So in this algorithm, the detected noised pixels, no matter ones with the lowest or highest gray value, are replaced by the median gray values or the morphological filtered ones. The flow chart is shown in Fig. 2.1(b). It is well known that the median filter is good at removing impulse noise. In mathematical morphology, opening operation is usually used to remove the pixels with higher gray value, while closing operation to remove those with lower gray value. So in this algorithm the noisy pixels are processed separately: the lowest gray value pixels using closing filter and the highest gray value ones using opening filter. Moreover, for simplicity, in experiments only one of the two operators (e.g., opening filter) is selected to process images and then their reverse ones.

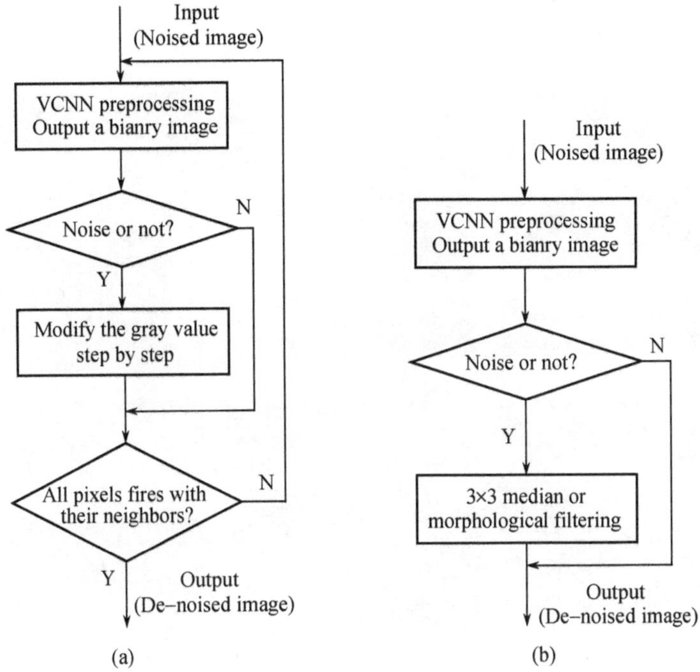

Fig. 2.1. (a) Flow chart of Algorithm I; (b) Flow chart of Algorithm II

2.2.3 Experimental Results and Analysis

Compared to the PCNN, the SCM simplifies internal activity to a single equation, so the SCM is much less time consuming than the PCNN. The SCM inherits both feeding and linking inputs consistent with the standard PCNN. Besides the feeding and the linking, the internal activity of the SCM has a term for recording the previous status using a leaky integrator. The ICM is the special case of the PCNN when there are no linking neurons. The ICM only has the feeding inputs. The SCM possesses the advantages of both the PCNN and the ICM, because it is simpler than the PCNN and more accurate than the ICM. Therefore, the SCM is preferable and effective. In the experiments of this chapter, the SCM is selected as the noise detection model. The performance of the SCM is compared with the parformances of neighborhood mean, median, and morphological filtering methods through simulation. These results are well illustrated in Fig. 2.2 and Table 2.1, and we can see that using the SCM the peak signal-to-noise ratio is improved greatly for impulse noise.

(a)
(b)
(c)
(d)
(e)
(f)
(g)
(h)
(i)
(j)
(k)
(l)

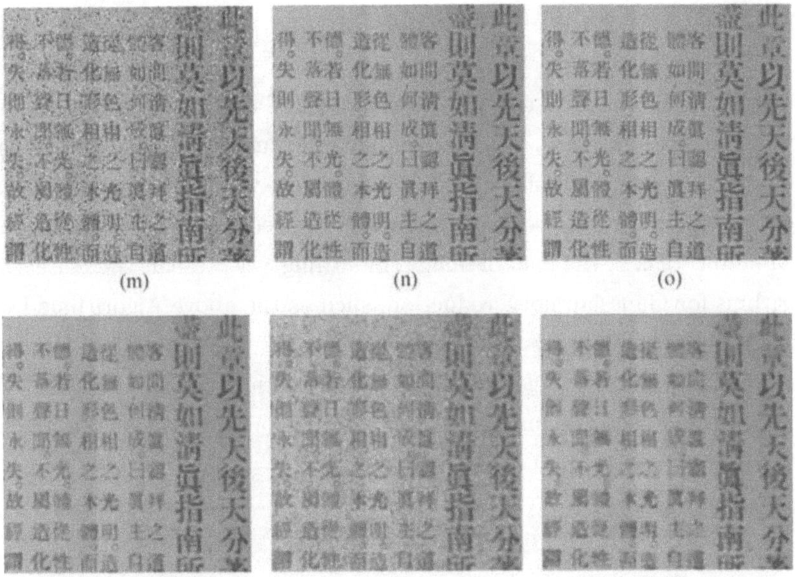

(m) (n) (o)

(p) (q) (r)

Fig. 2.2. Filtering results:(a) Lena with impulse noise of 5% density; (g) Cameraman with impulse noise of 10% density; (m) Characters with impulse noise of 5% density; (b/h/n) results of the SCM and median filtering; (c/i/o) results of the SCM and morphological filtering; (d/j/p) results of median filtering; (e/k/q) results of mean filtering, (f/l/r) results of morphological filter

From Figs. 2.1, 2.2 and Table 2.1, one can see that because the method of the SCM with a median or morphology filter only processes the detected noisy pixels, the details and edges of the image can be preserved well.

Table 2.1. Peak signal-to-noise ratio (dB) of the algorithms for impulse noise.

Methods	Algorithm II (SCM+Median)	Algorithm II (SCM+Morph)	Median	Mean	Morph
	Lena				
5%	41.997	41.125	31.393	25.704	28.772
10%	38.392	37.717	30.386	23.433	27.602
	Cameraman				
5%	38.289	38.768	26.772	23.522	24.568
10%	34.265	34.005	26.057	21.747	23.707
	Characters				
5%	36.763	37.703	25.411	23.565	23.988
10%	33.469	34.132	24.933	22.213	23.376

2.3 Gaussian Noise Filtering

As another main noise existing in digital images, Gaussian noise, a stationary ergodic stochastic process, is more complex and more common. If an image is contaminated by Gaussian noise, all its pixels would be changed, which makes it very difficult to remove the noise. The reduction of Gaussian noise is an onerous task in the field of image smoothing. At present, there are some algorithms for Gaussian noise reduction, such as the above Algorithms I and II, but the filtering effect is not very satisfying. In this subsection, the algorithm based on pulse-coupled neural networks with the null interconnection (PCNNNI) and the time matrix [7, 8] (called Algorithm III) is described.

2.3.1 PCNNNI and Time Matrix

For the basic PCNN model (Eqs.(1.11)–(1.15)), the characteristic of interconnection among neurons, that is $\beta \neq 0$, means that a neuron's firing can lead to the activation of its neighbors meeting given conditions, which weakens some of their information to a certain extent (for example, intensity). Taking $\beta = 0$ into consideration, a reduced model, pulse-coupled neural networks with the null interconnection, comes into being [9]. When processing images, each neuron relies on the separate information of itself, and the time matrix, recording the firing time of each neuron and indicating some information of the original image, can be built. When $\beta = 0$, the model becomes the following equations:

$$F_{ij}[n] = \exp(-\alpha_F)F_{ij}[n-1] + V_F Y_{ij}[n-1] + S_{ij}; \tag{2.5}$$

$$U_{ij}[n] = F_{ij}[n]; \tag{2.6}$$

$$Y_{ij}[n] = \begin{cases} 1 & if U_{ij}[n] > E_{ij}[n], \\ 0 & \text{Otherwise}; \end{cases} \tag{2.7}$$

$$E_{ij}[n] = \mathrm{e}^{-\alpha_E} E_{ij}[n-1] + V_E Y_{ij}[n\text{-}1]. \tag{2.8}$$

The model avoids the interaction between neurons. The firing time and firing frequency of each neuron is more related to the intensity of its responding pixels.

The differences in the intensity of image pixels lead to the differences in fire sequence. In order to store the firing time of each neuron, a time matrix $\boldsymbol{T}$, whose size is equivalent to the external input $\boldsymbol{S}$ and output $\boldsymbol{Y}$, can be defined. Besides, each element of $\boldsymbol{T}$ is corresponding to the neuron related to $\boldsymbol{S}$ and $\boldsymbol{Y}$. $\boldsymbol{T}$ can be described as

$$T_{ij}[n] = \begin{cases} n & if\ \ Y_{ij}[n] = 1, \\ T_{ij}[n-1] & \text{Otherwise.} \end{cases} \tag{2.9}$$

The time matrix is a mapping from the spatial image information to the time information, giving a genuine storage of the information about the firing time of each neuron. All possibilities are defected as: (1) the corresponding element value of $\boldsymbol{T}$ is set to "0" if the neuron has never fired; (2) the corresponding element value of $\boldsymbol{T}$ is set to n if the neuron fires for the first time at the time n; (3) the corresponding element value of $\boldsymbol{T}$ remains unchanged if the neuron has fired. The iteration goes on until all neurons have fired; leaving each element value of $\boldsymbol{T}$ nonzero.

The time matrix cannot only deliver the information about image segments and edge detection, but also can combine with other algorithms to achieve image de-noising and recognition. In a similar way, time matrix of the PCNNs can be taken.

Next, the algorithm based on the PCNNNI and the time matrix will be described in detail.

2.3.2 Description of Algorithm III

When the PCNNNI is used in the image denoising, firstly, each pixel's intensity of corrupted images is input to the corresponding neuron; secondly, the PCNNNI is run and the time matrix $\boldsymbol{T}$ is obtained. The smaller value elements of $\boldsymbol{T}$ correspond to the higher intensity pixels in the corrupted images because of the dynamic threshold function which decays in the time by the exponent term. Slide a window matrix $\boldsymbol{K}$ (3×3, each element is "1") on $\boldsymbol{T}$, determine the firing time of the neurons inside the window, and choose proper subsequent filtering methods to restore the corrupted images.

Gaussian noise is characterized by great density and extensive fluctuant range of noise intensity. That is to say, it not only influences the intensity of each pixel, but also has an obvious difference in the corrupting degree on the same intensity. Due to the aforementioned reasons, a single filter cannot do well in reducing noise. Here, a colligated filtering algorithm is proposed. A detailed flow chart is shown in Fig. 2.3, where the PCNNNI can be replaced by the ICM or SCM with no interconnection in this method.

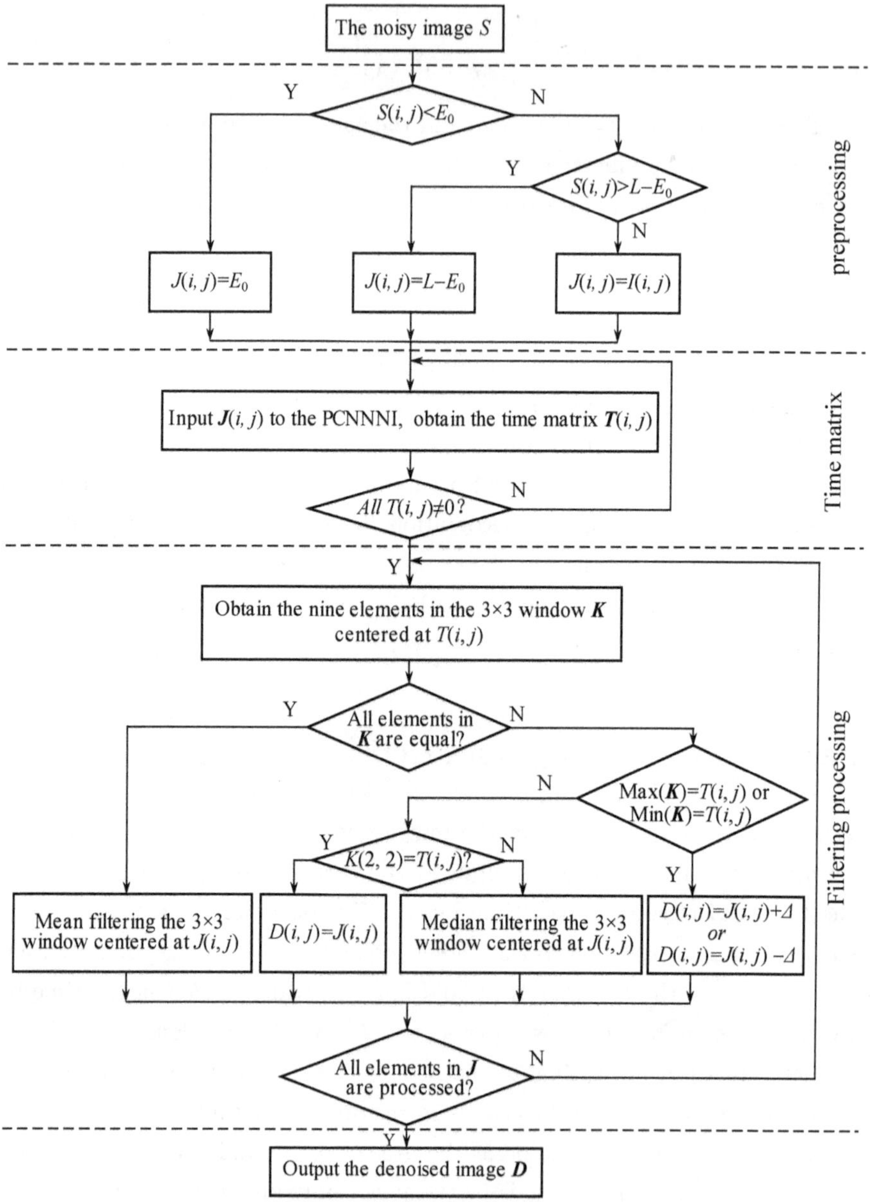

Fig. 2.3. Flow chart of Algorithm III

In Fig. 2.3, E_0 and L are a very small intensity and the possible maximum intensity (1 or 255). According to the fact that human visual system is insensitive to the slight variation in the image intensity, the preprocessing can reduce the image intensity range and shorten the iteration time of the PCNNNI. Δ is an intensity step length and is used to revise the value of pixels step by step.

The procedure of Algorithm III is listed as follows:

(1) Set the iteration time N, input the corrupted image and initialize feedback input F_{ij}, threshold E_{ij} and output Y_{ij}. At the same time, let each pixel be inactivated.

(2) Preprocess image $\boldsymbol{S}$ based upon the characteristic of human visual system. The detailed steps are shown as follows: put E_0 with a small value, set S_{ij} to E_0 if $S_{ij} < E_0$ and set S_{ij} to $L - E_0$ if $S_{ij} > L - E_0$ for all pixels in image $\boldsymbol{S}$.

(3) If N is presented, do iterative calculations of the preprocessed image according to Eqs. (2.5) – (2.8).

(a) If a neuron Ne_{ij} fires at iteration n, $Y_{ij}[n]$ outputs "1", and the corresponding element value in the time matrix $\boldsymbol{T}$ is set to n. Then set a very large threshold Ω(e.g., 10 000) for this neuron to make sure that it will never fire again.

(b) If a neuron Ne_{ij} does not fire at the time of the nth iteration, $Y_{ij}[n]$ outputs "0". The corresponding element value in the time matrix $\boldsymbol{T}$ remains unchanged, and the threshold of the neuron is determined by Eq. (2.8).

(4) If all elements of $\boldsymbol{T}$ are not "0", note down the iteration times N_1, and switch to (5); else, return to (3).

(5) Slide a 3×3 window matrix $\boldsymbol{K}$ (each element is "1") on $\boldsymbol{T}$, deal with the nine elements overlaid by $\boldsymbol{K}$ of $\boldsymbol{T}$ in turn, and choose proper subsequent filtering algorithms to restore the preprocessed corrupted image.

Rank the nine elements first:

(a) If the nine elements are equivalent to each other, the mean filter is used to process the preprocessed image.

(b) If the fifth element is equivalent to the central element overlaid by $\boldsymbol{K}$ in $\boldsymbol{T}$, the mean filter outputs the preprocessed image elements directly.

(c) If the first element is equivalent to the central element overlaid by $\boldsymbol{K}$ in $\boldsymbol{T}$, the output intensity of the corresponding element is subtracted by one step length Δ.

(d) If the ninth element is equivalent to the central element overlaid by $\boldsymbol{K}$ in $\boldsymbol{T}$, the output intensity of the corresponding element is added by one step length Δ.

(e) Otherwise, process the preprocessed image using the median filter.

(6) If all pixels have been processed, end; else, return to step (5).

2.3.3 Experimental Results and Analysis

Similarly, Algorithm III based on SCM is implemented and compared with Algorithm II based on SCM (SCM with median filter and with morphological filter) and the Wiener filter, and the results are shown in Fig. 2.4 and Table 2.2. It is observed that for image Lena, Algorithm III is better than Algorithm II, but for cameraman and characters, it is reverse. It is proven again that the Wiener filter is one of the best filters for Gaussian noise.

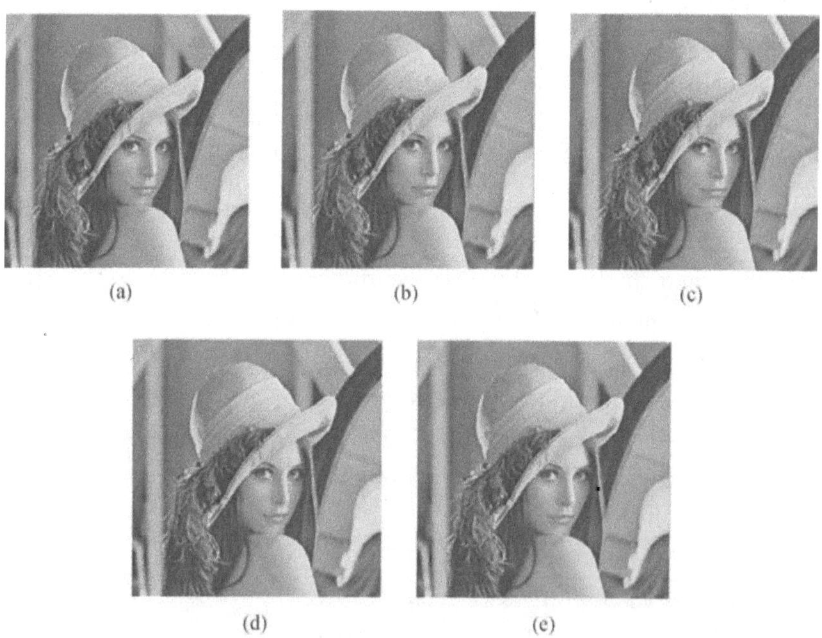

(a) (b) (c) (d) (e)

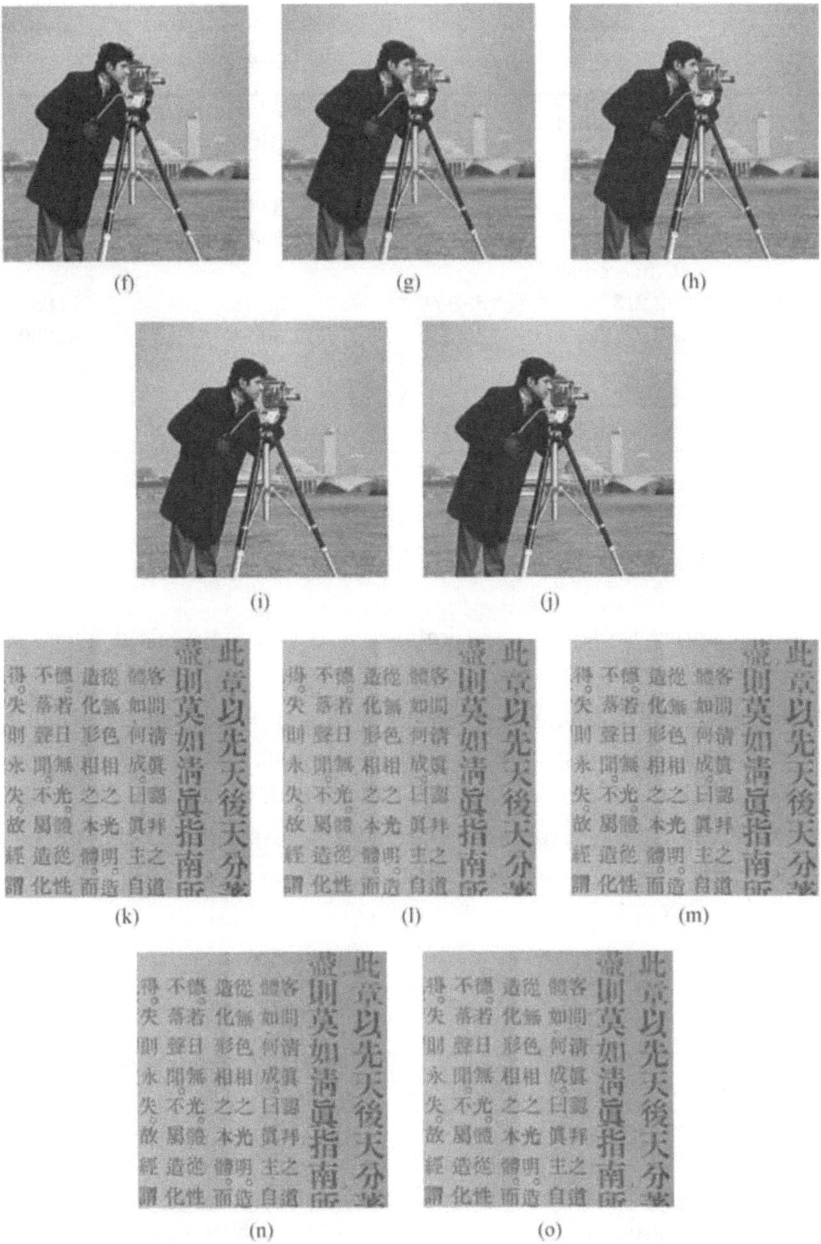

Fig. 2.4. Filtering results. (a) Lena with Gaussian noise of 0 mean and 0.0005 variance; (f) cameraman with Gaussian noise of 0 mean and 0.001 variance; (k) Characters with Gaussian noise of 0 mean and 0.0005 variance; (b/g/l) results of the SCM and time matrix; (c/h/m) results of the SCM and morphological filtering; (d/i/n) results of the SCM and median filtering; (e/j/o) results of Wiener filtering

Table 2.2. Peak signal-to-noise ratio (dB) of four algorithms: SCM and time matrix, SCM and median filter, SCM and morphological filter, and Wiener filter.

Methods	Algorithm III	Algorithm II (SCM+Morph)	Algorithm II (SCM+Median)	Wiener
	Lena			
(0,0.0005)	33.645 4	32.974 6	32.974 9	36.030
(0,0.001)	31.578 7	29.968 8	29.969 4	33.686 5
	Cameraman			
(0,0.0005)	32.213 3	33.171 6	33.182	36.087 2
(0,0.001)	30.945 3	30.221 1	30.237 6	33.630 4
	Characters			
(0,0.0005)	29.575 8	32.966 2	32.964 9	34.887 7
(0,0.001)	28.568 4	29.960 4	29.959 5	32.342 2

Summary

In this chapter, we smooth the impulse and Gaussian noised image with the PCNNs: PCNN, ICM, or SCM, combined with other classic algorithms, including the median algorithm, the step-by-step modifying algorithm and mathematical morphology. And the results are compared with other methods. Experimental results prove the good performance of the algorithms presented. Making full use of the output information of PCNNs and exploring the better restoring algorithms for impulse noise and Gaussian noise are our future work.

Reference

[1] Gonzalez RC, Woods RE (2002) Digital image processing, 2nd edn. Prentice Hall, Upper Saddle River, NJ.

[2] Ranganath HS, Kuntimad G, Johnson JL (1995) Pulse coupled neural networks for image processing. In: Proceedings of IEEE Southeast Conference, Raleigh, 26 – 29 March 1995

[3] Zhan K, Zhang HJ, Ma YD (2009) New spiking cortical model for invariant texture retrieval. IEEE Transactions on Neural Networks 20(12): 1980 – 1986

[4] Ma YD, Shi F, Li L (2003) A new kind of impulse noise filter based on PCNN. In: Proceedings of 2003 International Conference on Neural Networks and Signal Processing, Nanjing, 14 – 17 December 2003

[5] Ma YD, Zhang HJ (2008) New image denoising algorithm combined PCNN with gray-scale morphology. Journal of Beijing University of Posts and

Telecommunications 31(2): 108 – 112

[6] Ma YD, Zhang HJ (2007) A novel image de-noising algorithm combined ICM with morphology. In: Proceedings of the 7th International Symposium on Communications and Information Technologies, Sydney, 17 – 19 October 2007

[7] Ma YD, Shi F, Li L (2003) Gaussian noise filter based on PCNN. In: Proceedings of 2003 International Conference on Neural Networks and Signal Processing, Nanjing, 14 – 17 December 2003

[8] Ma YD, Lin DM, Zhang BD et al (2007) A novel algorithm of image Gaussian noise filtering based on PCNN time matrix. In: Proceedings of IEEE International Conference on Signal Processing and Communication, Dubai, 24 – 27 November 2007

[9] Lzhikevich EM (1998) Theoretical foundations of pulse-coupled models. In: Proceedings of the 1998 IEEE International Joint Conference on Neural Networks Part 3: IEEE World Congress on Computational Intelligence, Anchorage, 4 – 9 May 1998

Chapter 3 Image Segmentation

Image segmentation is a partitioning of an image into constituent parts according to its attributes such as pixel intensity, spectral values, and/or textural properties [1]. Image binarization segmentation which is defined as dividing an image into objects and background is the most fundamental and important processing step and common, basic and key technique in the research of object identification, image understanding and computer vision. The performance of image segmentation will impact directly on the subsequent object identification and image understanding. There are many methods of image segmentation and the simplest and most effective one is the method based on the gray-level threshold, but it is very difficult to select a appropriate threshold. In this chapter, two image segmentation approaches with PCNN: one based on entropy or cross-entropy and the other based on genetic algorithm (GA), are introduced.

3.1 Traditional Methods and Evaluation Criteria

Image binarization segmentation is defined as dividing an image into parts: object(s) and background. Traditional methods are based on a threshold decided according to pixel intensity, so the key is the appropriate selection of the threshold. Nowadays, a lot of research has been done and many methods, including the global threshold and local threshold, have been proposed [2 – 7]. The global threshold is simple, effective and fit for the images containing obvious differences between objects and background, while the local threshold is fitter for complex images or those with noise in their backgrounds than global one. Although the local threshold is flexible and can select thresholds adaptively, there are still some shortcomings, such as time-consuming and region of fracture and ghost in the segmented images.

In this subsection, three of traditional methods are described: the methods based on the arithmetic mean of the gray value [4], entropy and histogram of image [6], and maximum between-cluster variance [7]. Then several effect evaluation criteria are introduced.

3.1.1 Image Segmentation Using Arithmetic Mean

Mathematical expectation of random variable is a very important statistical feature. It reflects the average value of random variable, similar to object's center of mass. So dividing images according to the gray-level 'center' should be the best point of balance. The mathematical expectation of the gray images can be determined by the following equation:

$$\mu_{threshold} = \sum_{n=1}^{N} L_n P(L_n), \tag{3.1}$$

where L_n is the nth gray-level of the image, and $P(L_n)$ is the probability of L_n.

Let $h(L_n)$ be the number of L_n appearing in the image. Then

$$\begin{aligned} \mu_{threshold} &= \sum_{n=1}^{N} L_n P(L_n) \\ &= \sum_{n=1}^{N} L_n \frac{h(L_n)}{\sum\limits_{n=1}^{N} h(L_n)} \\ &= \sum_{n=1}^{N} L_n h(L_n) \Big/ \sum_{n=1}^{N} h(L_n). \end{aligned} \tag{3.2}$$

Equation (3.2) is a segmentation method based on the global threshold.

3.1.2 Image Segmentation Using Entropy and Histogram

Usually, when the gray-level distribution of objects in an image differs from that of the background significantly, two peaks may appear in its histogram and generally the more obvious trough is selected as the preferable threshold. In reality, because of the uneven gray-level distribution or noise existing in the image, there always exist a few and unobvious troughs in the histogram, which makes it difficult to get a reasonable threshold. Moreover, the trough is determined manually from the histogram, by which it is difficult to find out an ideal threshold.

It is well known that entropy, a statistical property of images, reflects the amount of information contained in images. For the majority of images, no matter whether segmentation method is employed, the greater the entropy of the segmented image, the more information can be obtained, the more details are included in the segmented image, and the better the total segmentation results should be. Here, the segmentation algorithm based on the maximum entropy and histogram of images is proposed.

For an image with a few troughs in the histogram, selecting each trough as the threshold, the segmented image with the maximum entropy is desired and its corresponding threshold is the best. The image entropy can be calculated as follows:

$$H(S) = -p_1 \ln p_1 - p_0 \ln p_0, \tag{3.3}$$

where p_1 and p_0 are the probabilities of 1 and 0 in the segmented image respectively.

3.1.3 Image Segmentation Using Maximum Between-cluster Variance

Variance is a measure of the gray-scale distribution homogeneity of images. The greater the variance is, the greater the difference between object(s) and a background is, while the difference between them will reduce when part of pixels in object(s) are divided into a background by error and vice versa, so the segmentation with maximal between-cluster variance means the smallest probability of the segmentation mistaken.

For an image, let T be the threshold and it is in the range from the minimum gray-level to the maximum; the ratio of the number of pixels in object(s) to the total is W_A and their average gray-level is μ_A; the ratio of the number of pixels in a background to the total is W_B and their average gray-level is μ_B; the average gray-level of the whole image is μ. Then the between-cluster variance is defined as

$$\sigma^2(T) = W_A(\mu_A - \mu)^2 + W_B(\mu_B - \mu)^2. \tag{3.4}$$

That is to say, the T, which results in the maximal between-cluster variance of the object(s) and background, is the best segmentation threshold.

3.1.4 Objective Evaluation Criteria

In this subsection, the gray-level uniformity measure (GU) [8], gray-level contrast (GC) [8], and shape measure (SM) [8] are selected as the objective evaluation criteria for testing the segmented images.

Gray-level Uniformity Measure

For a gray-level image $f(x,y)$, let R_i be ith segmented region, A_i be the area of R_i (that is the number of pixels contained in region R_i) and C be the normalization factor, then the gray-level uniformity measure of $f(x,y)$ is defined as

$$GU = 1 - \frac{1}{C}\sum_i \sum_{(x,y)\in R_i}\left[f(x,y) - \frac{1}{A_i}\sum_{(x,y)\in R_i} f(x,y)\right]^2. \tag{3.5}$$

Gray-level Contrast Measure

In a gray-level image $f(x,y)$ consisting of the object with the average gray-level f_o and the background with the average gray-level f_b, a gray-level contrast measure can be computed by

$$GC = \frac{|f_o - f_b|}{f_o + f_b}. \tag{3.6}$$

Shape Measure

Taking the form of a segmented region into account, the shape measure is defined as

$$SM = \frac{1}{C}\left\{\sum_{(x,y)} Sgn[f(x,y) - f_{N(x,y)}]g(x,y)Sgn[f(x,y) - T]\right\}, \tag{3.7}$$

where, $f_{N(x,y)}$ is the average gray-level of the neighborhood $N(x,y)$ of a pixel located at (x,y) with the gray-level $f(x,y)$ and gradient value $g(x,y)$, T is the threshold value for segmentation, C is a normalization factor and $Sgn()$ the unit step function.

Entropy and Cross-entropy

Entropy is a measure of uncertainty and information entropy describes the average amount of information included in all the objects in the source. Maximum entropy principle puts emphasis on the system uniformity and it is used in image segmentation to search for the threshold which results in as even as possible gray-level distribution inside the object(s) or background, as Eq. (3.3) shows. While the cross-entropy is a measure of information difference between two probability distributions [9]. The minimum cross-entropy principle is used in image segmentation to search for the threshold which results in the least information difference between the two images before and after segmentation.

For two probability distributions $P = \{p_1, p_2, ..., p_N\}$ and $Q = \{q_1, q_2, ..., q_N\}$, their cross-entropy is defined as [9]

$$D(P,Q) = \sum_{i=1}^{N} p_i \cdot \ln \frac{p_i}{q_i} + \sum_{i=1}^{N} q_i \cdot \ln \frac{q_i}{p_i}. \tag{3.8}$$

In an image segmentation, P and Q represent the original image and the segmented one respectively. Then

$$\begin{aligned} C(P,Q:t) = &\sum_{f=1}^{t} \left[f \cdot h(f) \cdot \ln \frac{f}{\mu_1(t)} + \mu_1(t) \cdot h(f) \cdot \ln \frac{\mu_1(t)}{f} \right] + \\ &\sum_{f=t+1}^{F} \left[f \cdot h(f) \cdot \ln \frac{f}{\mu_2(t)} + \mu_2(t) \cdot h(f) \cdot \ln \frac{\mu_2(t)}{f} \right], \end{aligned} \tag{3.9}$$

where, f is the gray-level, F is the maximal value of f, t is the threshold of segmentation and $h(f)$ is the histogram of original image. μ_1 and μ_2 are the average gray-level of objects and a background, respectively. They can be calculated by $h(f)$, shown as follows [10]:

$$\mu_1(t) = \frac{1}{\sum_{f=0}^{t} h(f)} \sum_{f=0}^{t} f \cdot h(f), \tag{3.10}$$

$$\mu_2(t) = \frac{1}{\sum_{f=t+1}^{F} h(f)} \sum_{f=t+1}^{F} f \cdot h(f). \tag{3.11}$$

3.2 Image Segmentation Using PCNN and Entropy

For image segmentation, each pulse image output from the PCNN with selected parameters properly can be thought to be a segmented image of the original one, but which is the best? If the iteration number N is predefined to be large enough. In this subsection, the maximum entropy principle or the minimum cross-entropy principle is applied to the determination of segmentation results. That is to say, for each pulse image, its entropy and the cross-entropy between itself and the original image are calculated, the one with the maximum entropy or minimum cross-entropy is the best segmentation.

Fig. 3.1. Results of the segmentation methods for Lena. (a) Original image; (b–f) the segmented image using (b) entropy and histogram of image; (c) arithmetic mean of gray levels; (d) maximum between-cluster variance; (e) minimum cross-entropy; (f) maximum entropy

All the segmentation methods mentioned above are compared and the results are shown in Fig. 3.1, Fig. 3.2, and Table 3.1. These methods are based on entropy and histogram of image (Me1), arithmetic mean of the gray levels (Me2), maximum between-cluster variance (Me3), minimum cross-

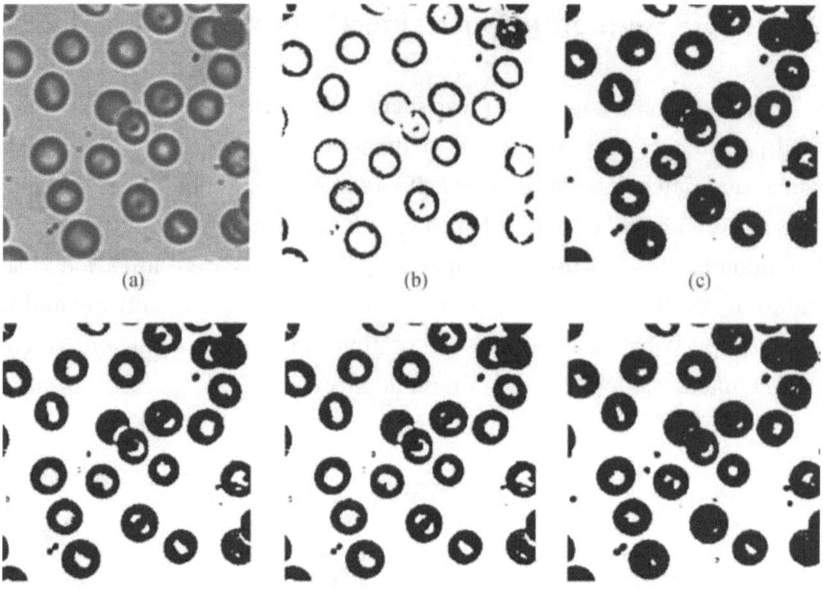

Fig. 3.2. Results of the segmentation methods for Blood. (a) Original image; (b–f) the segmented image using (b) entropy and histogram of image; (c) arithmetic mean of gray levels; (d) maximum between-cluster variance; (e) minimum cross-entropy; and (f) maximum entropy

entropy (Me4) and maximum entropy (Me5) respectively. In the same way as in Chapter 2, in the Me4 and Me5, the PCNN is replaced by the SCM, too. The four evaluation criteria—gray-level uniformity measure (GU), gray-level contrast measure (GC), entropy (En), and cross-entropy (Ce) are presented for these methods. In order to evaluate the performance of these four methods more comprehensively, here we just suggest another evaluating method, the overall merit (OM). In fact, it is the arithmetic mean of the GU, GC, En, and (1 – Ce), determined by Eq. (3.12) and the experimental results are listed in Table 3.1. For the Ce, the smaller the better, so for the GU, GC, En, and (1 – Ce), the larger the better, then the one with the largest OM is the best.

$$OM = [GU + GC + (1 - Ce) + En]/4. \tag{3.12}$$

In Fig. 3.1, the results of (b), (c), and (f) are better than (d) and (e); (d) and (e) are over-segmented slightly, although more details are obtained; (b) and (f) are better than (c) in the part of background edge. The experimental data OM in Table 3.1 can also prove the conclusion. In Fig. 3.2, (b), (d), and (e) are over-segmented and (b) is more obvious; (c) and (f) are better in vision. The results are also proven by the OM in Table 3.1. That is to say, the minimum cross-entropy principle is fitter for the image binarization segmentation.

Table 3.1. Comparison of the five methods based on entropy and histogram of image (Me1), arithmetic mean of gray levels (Me2), maximum between-cluster variance(Me3), minimum cross-entropy (Me4), and maximum entropy (Me5).

Images	Measures	Segmentation		methods		
		Me1	Me2	Me3	Me4	Me5
Lena	GU	0.988 8	0.989 2	0.989 5	0.988 9	0.988 8
	GC	0.315 0	0.328 5	0.346 2	0.367 6	0.315 0
	Ce	0.012 5	0.011 5	0.010 6	0.010 3	0.012 5
	En	0.999 8	0.996 0	0.977 4	0.938 2	0.999 8
	OM	0.822 8	0.825 6	0.825 6	0.821 1	0.822 8
Blood	GU	0.979 2	0.993 8	0.994 4	0.994 0	0.993 3
	GC	0.520 4	0.430 3	0.470 9	0.479 5	0.420 7
	Ce	0.020 3	0.007 0	0.005 3	0.005 3	0.007 7
	En	0.622 2	0.935 0	0.888 6	0.875 0	0.943 5
	OM	0.775 4	0.838 0	0.837 1	0.835 8	0.837 5

At last, the iteration number cross entropy and the iteration number of entropy are also shown in Fig. 3.3, in which the iteration number N is set to 35, the cross-entropy of each pulse image output from the PCNN and the

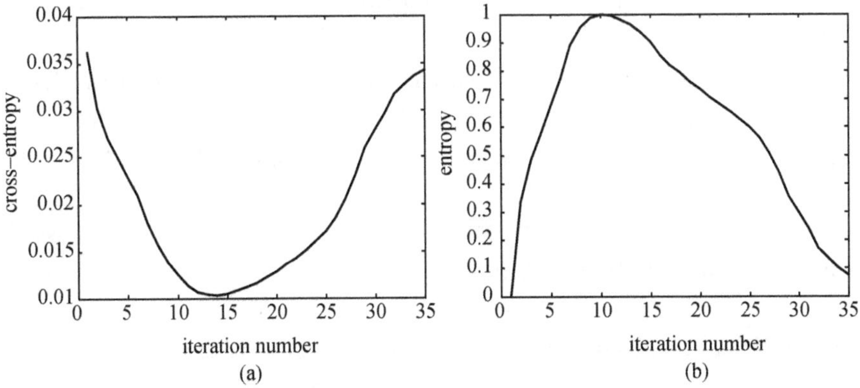

Fig. 3.3. Graphs of the situation of change of (a) cross-entropy and (b) entropy with the iteration time for Lena

original image is plotted in (a) and the entropy of each pulse image is shown in (b). From (a), the cross-entropy begins with a larger value, decreases quickly and reaches the minimum when iteration time is 14, then increases slowly. The situation of (b) is almost opposite to (a). The entropy increases quickly from 0 to the maximum, nearly 1, when the iteration time is 10 and then decreases slowly.

3.3 Image Segmentation Using Simplified PCNN and GA

Genetic Algorithm (GA) is a random optimization algorithm and was proposed drawing lessons from the natural selection and natural genetic mechanisms in the organic sphere. As a search algorithm which has the features of robustness, self-adaptive and parallelism, the GA has been widely used in the fields of image processing. The two main features of the GA, the population search strategy and the information interchange of individuals in population, can be omployed to obtain and accumulate the knowledge about the search space and control the process adaptively to obtain the optimal solution or approximate optimal solution during the search process. the GA operates in a more stochastic manner than the traditional search algorithm. This controllable randomness often allows the GA to find optimal solutions much quicker than their deterministic counterparts [11, 12].

The number of parameters to be determined will decrease if the PCNN model is simplified, but for a special image the key parameters are still needed to be selected by experiments or empirically. In this section, the GA and PCNN are combined effectively to display their own advantages. In other words, the capability of random search in the resolution space of the GA is used to find the optimum value of the PCNN key parameters to finish the setup of key parameters and image segmentation automatically.

3.3.1 Simplified PCNN Model

The PCNN is simplified and the typical model is listed as Eqs. (3.13) – (3.17).

$$F_{ij}[n] = S_{ij}; \tag{3.13}$$

$$L_{ij}[n] = \sum w_{ijkl} Y_{kl}[n-1]; \tag{3.14}$$

$$U_{ij}[n] = F_{ij}[n](1 + \beta L_{ij}[n]); \tag{3.15}$$

$$Y_{ij}[n] = \begin{cases} 1 & ifU_{ij}[n] > E_{ij}[n], \\ 0 & \text{Otherwise}; \end{cases} \tag{3.16}$$

$$E_{ij}[n] = \mathrm{e}^{-\alpha_E} E_{ij}[n-1] + V_E Y_{ij}[n-1]. \tag{3.17}$$

In this typical model, there are four key parameters left: $\boldsymbol{W}$, β, V_E, and α_E, in which $\boldsymbol{W}$ keeps unchanged and is usually set to the reciprocal of square distance between two pixels. The optimum value of the three parameters left needs to be found using the GA.

3.3.2 Design of Application Scheme of GA

The main problems needed to solve first are coding, designing fitness function and designing the three evolutionary operators (selection, crossover, and mutation) when the GA is applied. The set of initialization conditions and convergence conditions is the final work. After that, the optimal value of the parameter is able to be obtained by running the GA.

Coding

There are two main coding methods in the GA theory: binary coding and float coding. A large number of experiments show that there exists no difference in performance between these two methods [13]. The binary coding is adopted in the scheme for the optimal value by the GA because its parameters are less and it can be implemented more easily. The coding scheme is listed in Table 3.2.

Table 3.2. Chromosome composed of three genes.

gene	minimum	maximum	Coding length(bit)
Linking coefficient β	0.000 1	100	17
Amplitude coefficient V_E	0.000 1	400	19
Decay coefficient α_E	0.000 1	100	17

The overall coding length of chromosome is 53 bits.

Fitness Function

It is important to derive a suitable fitness function since the performance of the system mainly relies on the quality of the function. It is the fitness function that allows the GA to find the optimal solutions for problems where the optimum is unknown.

The entropy function shown as (3.3) is chosen as the object function in this subsection. To adjust the selection pressure and keep the variety of population, the fitness function is the power of object function as follows:

$$fitvalue = [H(S)]^k, \quad k = 1.004. \tag{3.18}$$

Selection

The best individual is retained in every generation according to the fitness proportion.

Crossover

The child-generation unlike parent-generation can be produced by crossover. The higher the probability of crossover, the more new structures in the population are produced, on the other hand, the lower the probability of crossover, the slower speed of convergence. Therefore, the double-point crossover is adopted and here the probability value is set to 0.7.

Mutation

Mutation can keep the variety of population efficiently. If the probability of mutation is too low, the information some genes carry may be lost, and will not be recovered, while if the probability of mutation is too high, the search of GA will become random search. Here the basic mutation operator is employed and the mutation probability is set to 0.01.

Size of Population

The evaluation number of fitness and the calculation complexity will increase if the size of population is big, but the phenomenon of immaturity convergence will arise if the size of population is small. So the value of size should be carefully chosen. Here, the value is set to 30; the max-generation is set to 50.

Stopping Criteria

All the evolutionary systems need a mechanism to stop training when a good solution is reached. The balance needs to be met so that the system will have enough time to generate useful data which should not be so many that the data become too specialized. The algorithm in this section will stop when one of following two conditions is satisfied:

(1) The variation of the max value of fitness is less than 0.001 within four consecutive generations.

(2) The max number of generations is reached.

To make the algorithm converge, the best-individual-keeping model is employed.

3.3.3 Flow of Algorithm

The flow of the proposed algorithm is as follows and the flow chart is shown in Fig. 3.4.

(1) Initialization: set the size of population $N = 30$, the number of generation $G = 50$, the probability of crossover $P_c = 0.7$, the probability of mutation $P_m = 0.01$, and the length of chromosome chromlength is 53 and read the input image. The initial population is produced randomly.

(2) Set $G = 1$, decode the 30 individuals and calculate the entropy of decoded images, and the fitness of individuals.

(3) Beginning the GA operation: selection with the best-individual-keeping, double-point crossover, and basic mutation.

(4) Decode the 30 individuals, Input to the improved the PCNN model, and calculate the entropy of output images and fitness of individuals.

(5) Evaluating the stopping criteria: if it is not satisfied, $G = G + 1$, go to (3).

(6) If yes, stop the algorithm and output the segmented image.

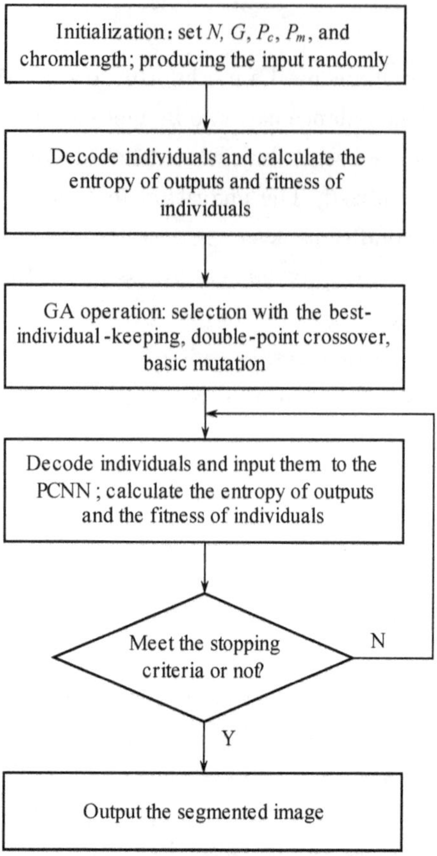

Fig. 3.4. Flow chart of the proposed algorithm

3.3.4 Experimental Results and Analysis

To test the proposed algorithm (Algorithm I) and compare it with the algorithm presented in [14] (Algorithm II), experiments are conducted on three images: Lena, bacteria, and cell.

The implementation condition of algorithm presented in [14] is: the linking strength $\beta = 0.2$, the linear decay, and the threshold decay constant $\Delta = 0.05$.

From Fig. 3.5, we can see that the results from Algorithm I are superior to Algorithm II in holding parts of face outline and hair detail comparing Lena (b) with (c). The result image from Algorithm I is good in detail and is well in the shape measure comparing bacteria and cell (h) with (i). The

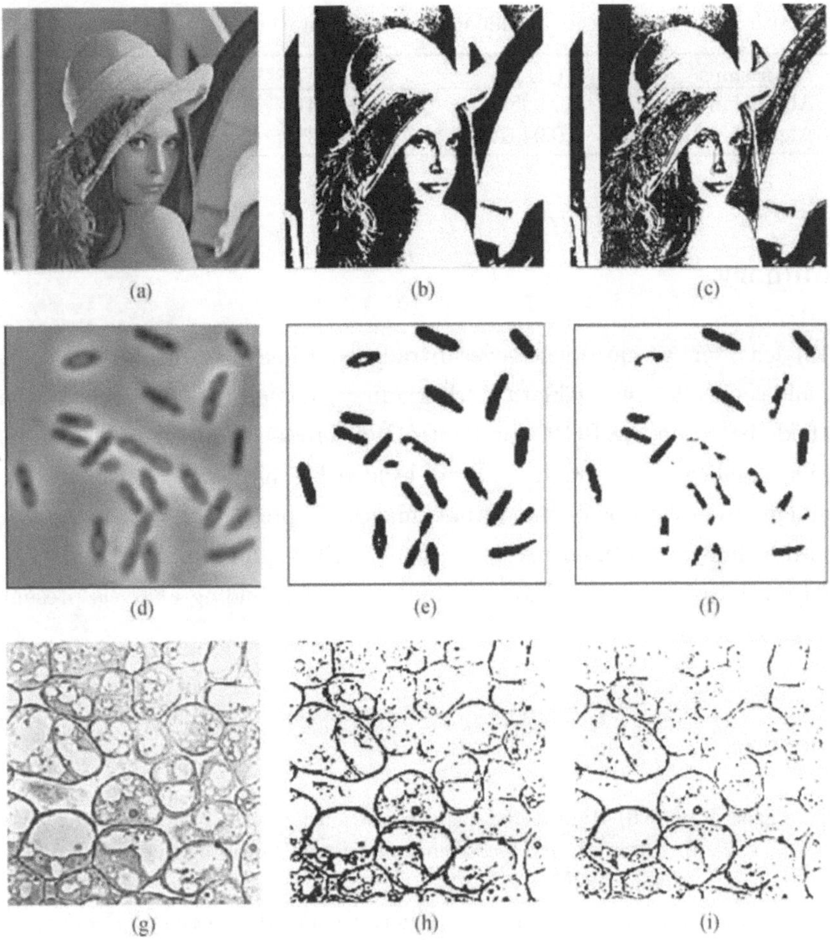

Fig. 3.5. Segmentation results. (a/d/g) Three original images: Lena, bacteria and cell; (b/e/h) segmented images using the proposed method; (c/f/i) segmented images using the method in Ref. [14]

segmented image obtained by Algorithm I is consistent with human visual characteristics. There exists over-segmentation using Algorithm II on the condition as follows: $\beta = 0.2$, the linear decay and $\Delta = 0.05$. If higher precision is required, parameter β still needs to be adjusted manually for Algorithm II. For bacteria, the GU, GC, or SM of Algorithm I is better than Algorithm II, as shown in Table 3.3.

Table 3.3. The objective evaluation of segmentation effect for bacteria.

Algorithms	GU	GC	SM
Algorithm I	0.99543	0.82414	0.76234
Algorithm II	0.94672	0.76853	0.75364

Summary

In this chapter, we introduce several traditional image segmentation methods and some effective evaluation criteria first; then automatic segmentation methods based on the PCNN and entropy or cross-entropy in which the iteration number of the PCNN can be decided by the maximum entropy or minimum cross-entropy of the output images are presented; at last, the GA is used to find the optimal parameters of the PCNN and implement the optimal image segmentation. Experiments and corresponding analysis present their good performances.

Reference

[1] Tilton JC (1996) Hybrid image segmentation for earth remote sensing data analysis. In: International Geoscience and Remote Sensing Symposium, Lincoln, 27 – 31 May 1996

[2] Long JY, Jin LW (2004) An image binarization method based on global mean and local standard deviation. Computer Engineering 30(2): 70 – 72

[3] Chen D, Zhang F, He GM (2003) An improved binarization algorithm for document image. Computer Engineering 29(13): 85 – 86

[4] Gao YY, Zhang L, Wu GW (1999) An algorithm for threshold based on arithmetic mean of gray value. Journal of Image and Graphics 4(6): 524 – 528

[5] Lu JZ (2004) The research on the binary image algorithm and its realization. Sci/tech Information Development & Economy 14(12): 266 – 267

[6] Su MJ, Chen R, Ma YD (2007) Research on the threshold segmentation algorithm based on entropy and histogram of image. China Science Paper Online. http://www.paper.edu.cn/advance_search. Accessed 11 October 2007

[7] Ostu N (1979) A threshold selection method from gray-level histograms. IEEE transactions on System, Man, and Cybernetics 9(1): 62 – 66

[8] Zhang YJ (1996) A survey on evaluation methods for image segmentation. Pattern recognition 29(8): 1335 – 1346

[9] Ranganath HS, Kuntimad G (1999) Object detection using pulse coupled neural networks. IEEE Transactions on Neural Networks 10(3): 615 – 620

[10] Li CH, Lee CK (1993) Minimum cross-entropy thresholding. Pattern Recognition 26(4): 617 – 625

[11] Rechenberg I (1965) Cybemetic solution path of an experimental problem. Royal Aircraft Establishment, Library translation No. 1222, Farnborough, Hants., U.K.

[12] Schwefel HP (1981) Numerical optimization of computer model. Wiley, Chichester

[13] Li MQ, Kou JS, Li D et al (2002) Basic theory and application of GA. Science Press, Beijing

[14] Gu XD, Guo SD, Yu DH (2002) A new approach for image segmentation based on unit-linking PCNN. In: The 1st International Machine Learning and Cybernetics Conference, Beijing, 4 – 5 November 2002

Chapter 4 Image Coding

The large amount of data bring difficulties for storage and transmission of digital images. For instance, a typical uncompressed scanned image of size $2\ 480 \times 3\ 500$ will take up approximately 25 megabytes of storage space. The data compression techniques have been used to reduce the amount of data required by representing an image with no or little distortion as far as possible. It means that the digital data contain much redundancy, which is of no or little use for image representation. The aim of information coding is to represent the effective information accurately with less code.

The traditional compression methods, like run-length coding, Huffman coding, and arithmetic coding, usually only achieved a low compression ratio while achieving a higher ratio maybe at the expense of image quality. These methods work on linear correlation between image data and try to eliminate redundancy but ignore features of images, such as the shape, texture, edge, and some factors from physiology, psychology, and Human Visual System (HVS).

The image compression methods based on block coding, such as the JPEG[1], H.261[2], and MPEG[3, 4], get widely used because they have low computation complexity and especially do not need any shape information of objects in the original image. However, there exist some inherent shortages in this kind of methods, such as the mosaic effect, the objectionable block distortion that greatly affects the subjective quality of reconstructed image and low compression ratios.

At the same time the second-generation image compression techniques [5, 6] based on the HVS can achieve high compression ratios through identifying and making use of the features in the image while still maintaining the image quality. Among these techniques, the Segmented Image Coding (SIC) [7] is thought to be a promising technique. The SIC is a region-oriented coding, which attempts to separate an image into some regions with slowly varying image intensity by image edges, then applies appropriate coding techniques to each region and contour, respectively.

4.1 Irregular Segmented Region Coding

Based on HVS, the Irregular Segmented Region Coding (ISRC), which partitions an image into similar regions with slowly varying intensity so that the image can be well encoded according to different structures of the original image, is no longer limited to a simple transform coding, for example, block transform coding (DCT and FFT) which partitions the initial image into square blocks with the same size of $2^n \times 2^n$. Therefore, the ISRC gets a better subjective visual quality of the reconstructed image than the JPEG method in which there exists serious distortion in reconstructed image, for instance, blocking artifacts, as shown in Fig. 4.1(c). And it will be able to achieve a higher compression ratio than traditional methods.

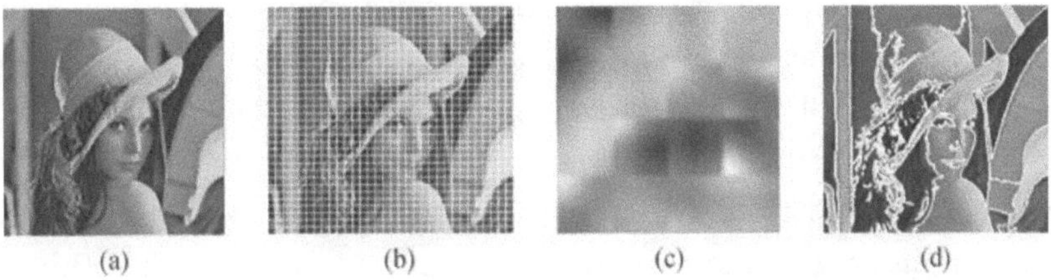

Fig. 4.1. (a) Original image; (b) block transform based coding; (c) blocking artifacts; (d) irregular segmented region coding

A segmentation-based compression technique is mainly realized through three steps [8]:

- preprocessing
- segmentation
- coding of contours and texture components

The purpose of preprocessing is to eliminate some tiny regions that slightly affect the coding quality, to enhance the image and remove noise produced in the sampling process. Segmentation assembles similar pixels into corresponding regions and separates those regions with dissimilar pixels. The SIC techniques depend on this kind of segmentation methods which have been explored for decades, and it is the segmentation method that determines the coding manner of SIC [8]. In this chapter, a new kind of segmentation image coding method based on the PCNN, named the Irregular Segmented Region Compression Coding Based on the PCNN (ISRCCBP), is adopted and will be described specially in Section 4.2. The relevant knowledge of image denoising and segmentation has been presented in Chapters 2 and 3. The image enhancement will be discussed in Chapter 5. And the last step coding of contours and texture components, will be explored in this chapter in detail.

In the ISRC, the image is partitioned into regions with slowly varying intensity, while the image intensity inside a region is approximated by a linear combination of some groups of orthogonal basis-functions, and some groups of orthogonal polynomials are adopted in this chapter. Such orthogonal polynomials must be generated for every single region of the input image, and their coefficients mainly depend on the corresponding intensity of the region. To code contour pixels and locate every region in the partitioned image, the contour coding is necessary, which is achieved usually by dint of the chain code because of the irregularity of segmented regions.

In this section, the principle of the irregular segmented region coding and decoding by means of these orthonormal basis-functions is mainly investigated in detail. The ISRCCBP will be more suitable for the segmented regions and natural edge of objects in the original image. It much better matches the HVS [5] and will not only be able to achieve higher compression ratios but also obtain the reconstructed image with better quality. Principle and experimental results based on the ISRCCBP will be presented in next section.

4.1.1 Coding of Contours Using Chain Code

As stated above, an image is mainly partitioned into two types of portions: homogeneous regions and contours which separate the image into regions. So in order to decode the image in the receiver, the position of the region in the image must be recorded. Obviously, it will be efficient to record the closed contours. The most often used method for representing these contours is chain code.

The chain code gets more widely used because of its good performance of representing different shapes of objects such as lines, planar curves, and contours. The most commonly used method called Freeman chain code was proposed by Freeman in 1961[9]. And it follows well the contour of a segmented object in a clockwise manner and keeps track of the directions as it travels from one contour pixel to another. The direction of each movement is encoded by a series of numbers, from 0 to 7, denoting an angle shown in Fig. 4.2(c). The codes associated with four or eight possible directions are the chain codes, and with the current contour pixel position as the center. In addition, 2 bits (00 – 11) will be needed to represent a possible direction when four-neighbor is used while 3 bits (000 – 111) will be needed for eight-neighbor which contains the smaller number of chain.

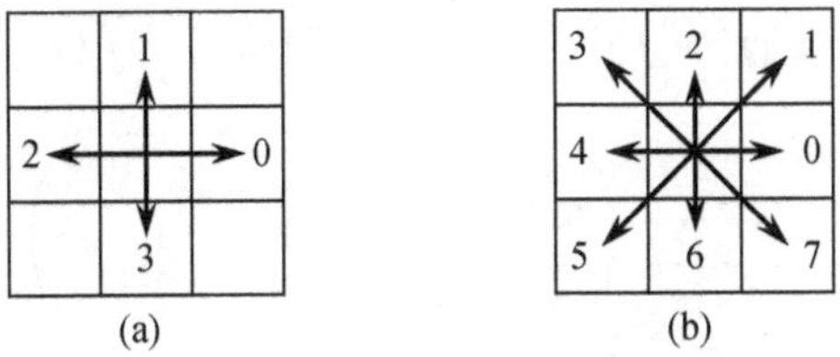

Fig. 4.2. Freeman chain code in four directions (a) and in eight directions (b)

Figure 4.3(a) shows that the chain code for the enlarged object contour from top to bottom is $\{2, 3, 3, 3, 0, 0, 3, 0\}$, associated with four directions, and a total of 8×2 bits $= 16$ bits is needed, while the code associated with eight directions is $\{5, 6, 7, 0, 7\}$, and a total of 5×3 bits $= 15$ bits is needed, as shown in Figs. 4.3(b) and 4.3(c), respectively. It shows that eight directions coding may require fewer codes than four directions coding for a certain length contour.

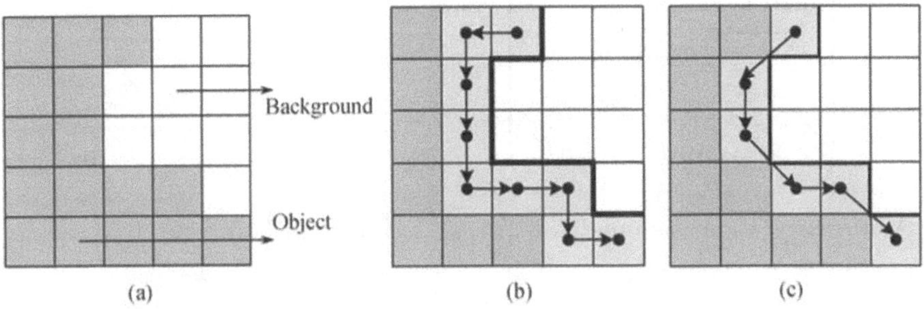

Fig. 4.3. Freeman chain coding example (a) Object (region shaded) to be studied and its background (b) Freeman chain code in four directions (c) Freeman chain code in eight directions

4.1.2 Basic Theories on Orthogonality

Let $f(x,y)$ denote the intensity of pixel corresponding to coordinate (x,y), $f'(x,y)$ is the approximating function of $f(x,y)$, and it can be represented by weighted sums of N orthogonal basis-functions $\{\varphi_1,\varphi_2,...,\varphi_N\}$ which are parameterized by their corresponding coefficients $\{\alpha_1,\alpha_2,...,\alpha_N\}$.

$$f'(x,y)=\sum_{i=1}^{N}\alpha_i\varphi_i\left(x,y\right). \tag{4.1}$$

The error function can be defined as

$$\begin{aligned}E=\left\|f'-f\right\|^2&=\sum_y\sum_x\left(f'\left(x,y\right)-f\left(x,y\right)\right)^2\\&=\sum_y\sum_x\left(\sum_{i=1}^{N}\left(\alpha_i\varphi_i\left(x,y\right)\right)-f\left(x,y\right)\right)^2.\end{aligned} \tag{4.2}$$

To minimize E by α, for $\forall i$, let $\partial E/\partial\alpha_i=0$, and the result is shown as follows:

$$\begin{pmatrix}\sum\limits_y\sum\limits_x\varphi_1\left(x,y\right)\varphi_1\left(x,y\right) & \cdots & \sum\limits_y\sum\limits_x\varphi_N\left(x,y\right)\varphi_1\left(x,y\right)\\ \sum\limits_y\sum\limits_x\varphi_2(x,y)\varphi_2(x,y) & \cdots & \sum\limits_y\sum\limits_x\varphi_N(x,y)\varphi_2(x,y)\\ \vdots & & \vdots\\ \sum\limits_y\sum\limits_x\varphi_1\left(x,y\right)\varphi_2\left(x,y\right) & \cdots & \sum\limits_y\sum\limits_x\varphi_2\left(x,y\right)\varphi_N\left(x,y\right)\end{pmatrix}\begin{pmatrix}\alpha_1\\ \alpha\\ \vdots\\ \alpha_N\end{pmatrix}$$
$$=\begin{pmatrix}\sum\limits_y\sum\limits_x f\left(x,y\right)\varphi_1\left(x,y\right)\\ \sum\limits_y\sum\limits_x f(x,y)\varphi_2(x,y)\\ \vdots\\ \sum\limits_y\sum\limits_x f\left(x,y\right)\varphi_N\left(x,y\right)\end{pmatrix}. \tag{4.3}$$

And then, if the basis functions $\varphi_1,\varphi_2,...,\varphi_N$ are orthonormal, that means,

$$\sum_y\sum_x\varphi_i\left(x,y\right)\varphi_j\left(x,y\right)=0,\quad\forall i\neq j \tag{4.4}$$

and

$$\sum_y\sum_x\varphi_i\left(x,y\right)\varphi_i\left(x,y\right)=1,\quad\forall i. \tag{4.5}$$

Then α_i can be obtained from

$$\alpha_i = \sum_y \sum_x f(x, y)\varphi_i(x, y) \quad 1 \leqslant i \leqslant N. \tag{4.6}$$

4.1.3 Orthonormalizing Process of Basis Functions

As proved in Ref. [10], in an N-dimensional subspace, a set of orthonormal basis functions always can be gotten from a set of linearly independent initial basis using the orthonormalization scheme of Gram-Schmidt. The next is the main principle:

Let U be the union of the point of (x, y), the inner product between two functions on U is defined as

$$< f,\ g > = \sum_{x,y} f(x, y)g(x, y) \quad (x, y \in U). \tag{4.7}$$

If $< f, g >$ is zero, then $f(x, y)$ and $g(x, y)$ are orthogonal. A set of normal orthonormal function $\{\varphi_0, \varphi_1, ..., \varphi_N\}$ can be obtained by Gram-Schmidt in case that $\{\phi_0, \phi_1, ..., \phi_N\}$ are linearly independent initial basis functions.

$$\varphi_j = \sum_{i=0}^{j} c_{j,i}\phi_i, \tag{4.8}$$

where $j = 0, ..., N$ and $c_{j,j} \neq 0$. The first normal orthonormal function φ_0 could be gotten by normalizing ϕ_0, that is $\varphi_0 = \phi_0/||\phi_0||(||\phi_0||$ denotes the usual 2-norm of $\phi_0)$ and φ_1 can be computed as

$$N_1\varphi_1 = \phi_1 - d_{1,0}\varphi_0, \tag{4.9}$$

where, $N_1 = ||\phi_1 - d_{1,0}\varphi_0||$, $d_{1,0}$ is equal to $< \phi_1, \varphi_0 >$ because ϕ_1 and φ_0 are orthonormal. The rest may be deduced similarly:

$$N_n\varphi_n = \phi_n - \sum_{i=0}^{n-1} < \phi_n, \varphi_i > \varphi_i \quad 1 < n \leqslant N, \tag{4.10}$$

$$N_n = ||\phi_n - \sum_{i=0}^{n-1} < \phi_n, \varphi_i > \varphi_i|| \quad 1 < n \leqslant N. \tag{4.11}$$

So far, a set of standard orthonormal functions $\{\varphi_0, \varphi_1, ..., \varphi_N\}$, by Gram-Schmidt, has been gotten from a set of linearly independent initial basis functions $\{\phi_0, \phi_1, ..., \phi_N\}$.

Suppose that the naturally ordered binomials $1, x, y, x^2, xy, y^2, x^3, x^2y, ...$, act as the linearly independent initial basis. With the help of orthonormalization of the initial basis, the orthonormal basis could be gotten for every segmented region and the approximating function can be expressed as Eq. (4.1) [11].

The orthonormal functions cannot be all listed here because of the large amount of functions. An instance of orthonormal functions is shown as follows:

$$
\begin{aligned}
\varphi_0 &= +0.022930, \\
\varphi_1 &= +0.162676 + 0.000894x, \\
\varphi_2 &= -0.963731 + 0.001062x + 0.003246y, \\
\varphi_3 &= +0.852345 - 0.011972x + 0.000934y + 0.00033x^2, \\
\varphi_4 &= 10.153461 - 0.070308x - 0.033635y + 0.000070x^2 + 0.000192xy, \\
\varphi_5 &= +0.102444 + 0.048782x - 0.035872y - 0.000061x^2 - 0.000115xy + \\
&\quad 0.000116y^2.
\end{aligned}
$$

For simplicity, the naturally ordered binomials with the highest degree of two are adopted. That is to say, $N = 6$, and the initial basis will be 1, x, y, x^2, xy, and y^2.

The codes of N coefficients of orthonormal polynomial are the ones of image regions; these coefficients are calculated according to the intensity of pixels corresponding to regions.

In general, the larger the N is, the better the reconstructed image will be. In addition, this characteristic makes progressive image coding (or reconstruction) possible, and an image can be browsed in the rough for a smaller N or get more details for a larger N.

It was found that much less computer memory was needed to store the coefficients than the original image, resulting in data compression. Therefore, it is desirable to describe the image by means of a small number of dominating features.

4.1.4 ISRC Coding and Decoding Framework

In brief, in the ISRC, the contours can be coded with chain code while regions can be expressed approximately with a set of weighted orthogonal basis functions. An image $f(x, y)$ can be expressed with an approximate function $f'(x, y)$ which can be built through a set of arbitrary linearly independent basis functions $\{\phi_0, \phi_1, ..., \phi_N\}$.

The framework of ISRC algorithm is shown in Fig. 4.4, and the coefficients of orthogonal basis function, the final polynomial, are quantized and coded for each segmented region. Then coefficients codes combining with the contour codes (chain codes) which depict the position of corresponding regions act as the image codes. And at the receiver in Fig. 4.5, the image is reconstructed through the function $f'(x, y)$ built by the coefficients of each region and contour codes.

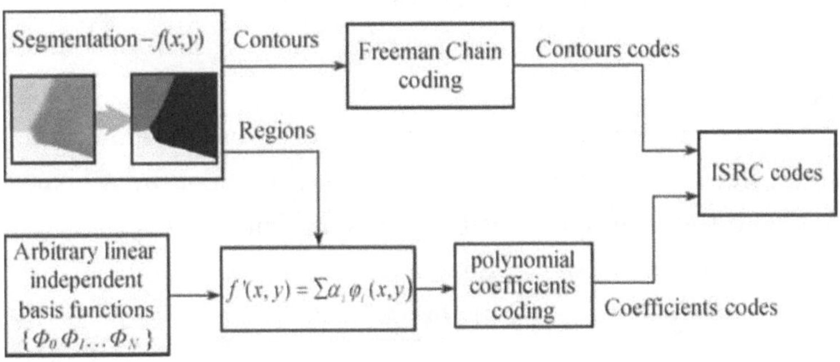

Fig. 4.4. Framework of the irregular segmented region coding (ISRC)

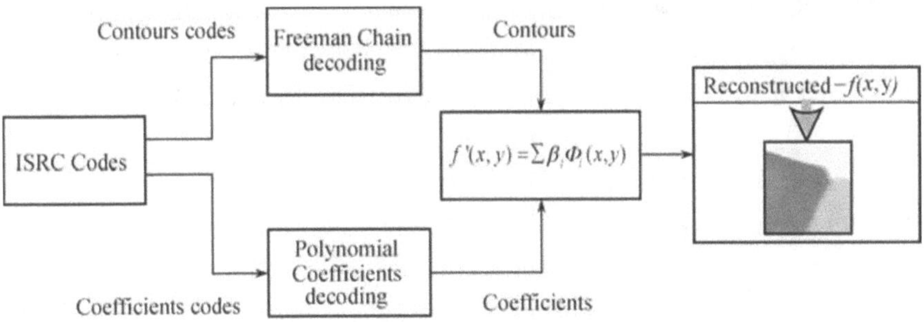

Fig. 4.5. Framework of the irregular segmented region decoding

4.2 Irregular Segmented Region Coding Based on PCNN

In this section, a segmented image coding method named irregular segmented region coding based on the PCNN is proposed. A lot of experimental results are listed to show its performance.

4.2.1 Segmentation Method

In the SIC, the main step is segmentation. The optimal segmentation algorithm, which should partition the original image into disjoint regions R_j with similar properties, is the key factor in the SIC. In order to improve the quality of image coding, the segmentation method adopted in the SIC should satisfy the following conditions and properties:

(1) Be able to control the number of partition regions;

(2) In order to obtain a well reconstructed image, each region should have the characteristics of the gray level similarity;

(3) Be able to generate smooth contours and avoid pseudo-contours.

The degree of similarity is evaluated for each region by a homogeneity criterion used to judge the intensity approximation.

That is, each pixel of the original image exactly belongs to one region R_j, supposing that I denotes all pixels in an image,

$$I = \bigcup_{\forall j} R_j \quad and \quad R_j \cap R_k = \varnothing \quad \forall j \neq k. \tag{4.12}$$

The PCNN emulates the mammalian visual cortex, which implies that it is one of the most efficient image processing methods [12, 13]. The output of the PCNN is a series of pulse images [14, 15]. The PCNN model is described as Eqs. (1.11) – (1.15) in Chapter 1.

A two-dimensional image with size of $M \times N$ can be thought to be a PCNN network with $M \times N$ neurons [16 – 18], and the intensity of pixels can be thought to be its stimulus, and the input of the neuron.

A firing neuron may result in the synchronous firing of its neighbors with approximate intensity. The output contains features of stimulus such as the edge, texture and regional information. Then the output is the segmented image. Therefore, the PCNN can be applied to image segmentation [14, 15].

Because the SIC adopts the PCNN segmentation and the coefficients of the final polynomial corresponding to regions are coded together with contour code, it is named the Irregular Segmented Region Compression Coding Based on the PCNN (ISRCCBP).

4.2.2 Experimental Results and Analysis

In this subsection, the performance of the ISRCCBP (Algorithm II) is compared with the commonly used method known as the 2D-DCT (Algorithm I), the classical one used in the JPEG, MPEG1, and MPEG2. As shown in Fig. 4.6 (a_1-a_3), Lena, House and Milkdrop of 128 × 128, and 8 bits are used as test images. The reconstructed images are shown in Fig. 4.6 (b_1-b_3) and (c_1-c_3), at the same time the Peak Signal to Noise Ratio (PSNR) and Compression Rate (CR) of experiments are shown in Table 4.1.

Fig. 4.6. Reconstructed image

Peak Signal to Noise Ratio (PSNR) used to measure quality of reconstructed image is defined as

$$\mathrm{PSNR} = 10 \times \lg \frac{255^2}{\frac{1}{MN}\sum_{i=0}^{M-1}\sum_{j=0}^{N-1}\left[I(i,j) - I'(i,j)\right]^2}, \tag{4.13}$$

where $I(i,j)$ and $I'(i,j)$ are the intensity of the original image and reconstructed image, respectively corresponding to coordinates (i,j); M and N mean the number of rows and columns of image.

Compression Ration (CR) can be calculated as

$$\mathrm{CR} = \frac{n}{n_c + n_o}, \tag{4.14}$$

where, n is the number of bits to figure the original image; n_c denotes the number of bits used to code the coefficients of the orthonormal basis function. and n_o is number of bits except n_c for the reconstructed image.

Table 4.1. PSNR (dB) and CR of both algorithms.

	Lena		Milkdrop		House	
	CR	PSNR(dB)	CR	PSNR(dB)	CR	PSNR(dB)
ISRCCBP	14.9	32.74	14.11	33.61	21.6	34.31
2D-DCT	13.6	29.90	10.7	29.10	11.7	28.37

At the approximate CR, the PSNR of Algorithm II is much higher than 2D-DCT (Algorithm I). The blocks zoomed to 400% shown in Fig. 4.6 (d1 – d3) present serious block distortion known as mosaic effect, the pseudo-contours, while Fig. 4.6 (e1 – e3) contains no such mosaic effect that destroys the natural edges and contours of objects and background in the original image. It means the performance of the Algorithm II is superior to the Algorithm I because the former can better retain the edges and details of the image, and the ISRCCBP performs better in the image compression.

In terms of the theory of exhaustive orthonormal set, the value of N, and the number of Schmidt initial basis may not be arbitrary; it could be 1, 3, 6, 10, 15, 21, 28, ... The experimental results shown in Fig. 4.6 and Table.4.1 are obtained when $N = 6$, while Fig. 4.7 and Table 4.2 are obtained when $N = 3$, 6, 10, 15, and 21.

Table 4.2. PSNR (DB) with different N.

	$N = 3$	$N = 6$	$N = 10$	$N = 15$	$N = 21$
PSNR(dB)	27.8376	28.5842	29.1904	29.1413	27.9052

Fig. 4.7 (b) shows 210 disjoint regions, and the segmentation of Fig. 4.7 (a) is conducted by means of the ISRCCBP. Investigation of the quality of the constructed images shown in Fig. 4.7(c – g) with the algorithm II for different N presents that the quality of reconstruction image becomes better and better with the increase of N.

At the same time, it should be noted that the quality of the reconstructed image becomes much better; especially edges, contours or details are recon-

Fig. 4.7. Reconstructed image with different N. (a) Lena; (b) regions label; (c) $N = 3$; (d) $N = 6$; (e) $N = 10$; (f) $N = 15$; (g) $N = 21$

structed more clearly when increasing the number of orthonormal basis.

It is demonstrated that the ISRCCBP much more matches the HVS being more sensitive to contours than the details of an image.

In addition, the change of PCNN parameters affects the performance of the ISRCCBP. The experiments shown in Fig. 4.8 and Table 4.4 are based on Parameters I and II (Table 4.3).

Table 4.3. Parameter I and Parameter II.

	α_E	β
Parameter I	0.1	0.4
Parameter II	0.3	0.3

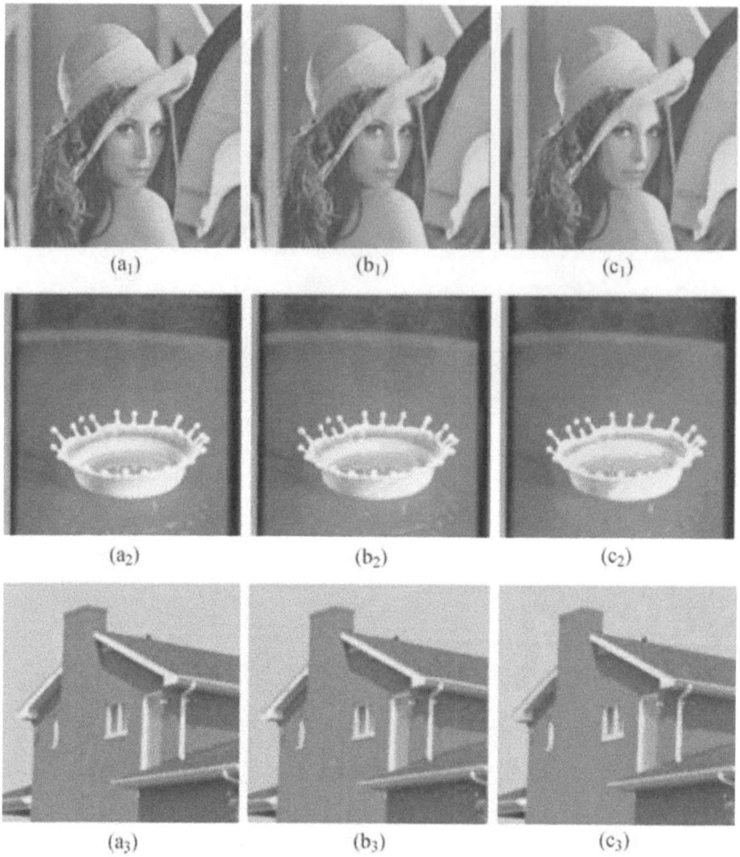

Fig. 4.8. Reconstructed images with different parameters. (a) original images, (b) and (c) reconstructed images with Parameter I and Parameter II, respectively

It can be seen that the number of regions in segmented image decreases with the increase of α_E as shown in Fig. 4.8 and Table 4.4 corresponding to the decreasing of the PSNR because of the rapid change of the PCNN threshold, and obviously CR increases synchronously, too. Thus, the performance of ISRCCBP becomes worse.

Table 4.4. Coding characteristics with different parameters.

Parameters	Lena			Milkdrop			House		
	M	CR	PSNR (dB)	M	CR	PSNR (dB)	M	CR	PSNR (dB)
I	367	14.88	32.74	367	14.11	33.61	253	21.59	34.31
II	283	19.30	30.91	199	27.44	30.01	222	24.60	25.88

∗ M denotes the number of regions in segmented image.

It means CR could be controlled by the chosen parameters of the PCNN depending on the special application.

As shown in Table 4.5, some experiments explored the relation between the CR and image resolution, based on the platform of Pentium IV/CPU 2.4 GHz/ 1024 MB RAM, and Microsoft Visual C++ 6.0. The test images are Lena, House and Milkdrop of $128 \times 128, 256 \times 256, 512 \times 512$, and 768×768, and of 8 bits, respectively.

Table 4.5. Coding characteristics of different resolution based on ISRCCBP [19].

Images	Resolutions	CR	PSNR(dB)	Time t(s)
Lena	128×128	14.22	29.79	≈0
	256×256	14.89	32.74	4
	512×512	15.11	32.35	57
	768×768	33.99	30.51	119
Milkdrop	128×128	11.47	31.68	≈0
	256×256	14.11	33.61	4
	512×512	18.88	34.69	47
	768×768	34.30	37.65	121
House	128×128	19.79	32.05	≈0
	256×256	21.59	34.31	4
	512×512	26.16	33.44	38
	768×768	29.33	34.99	138

It can be noticed that with the increase of the original image resolution, CR is increasing evidently with the almost non-decreasing PSNR but the more time obviously. It means that the ISRCCBP maybe better suits the compression of the higher resolution image than the lower one. However, the algorithm is time-consuming when the resolution is the higher, which could be resolved with the optimization of the ISRCCBP algorithm and the special fast processing devices such as Digital Signal Processor (DSP). The experiment will be discussed as follows.

The implement of the ISRCCBP is investigated on the DSP platform of TMS320C6713 as shown in Fig. 4.9. TMS320C6713 is one of the members of C67x family of TI Company, it is a 32-floated DSP based on an advanced modified Harvard architecture having one 32-bit high-performance External Memory Interface (EMIF). The algorithm of the ISRCCBP is realized with the optimized C code, such as the optimization of the data type, circulation programming, and some similar strategies.

Table 4.6 only shows the changes of executing cycles and time before

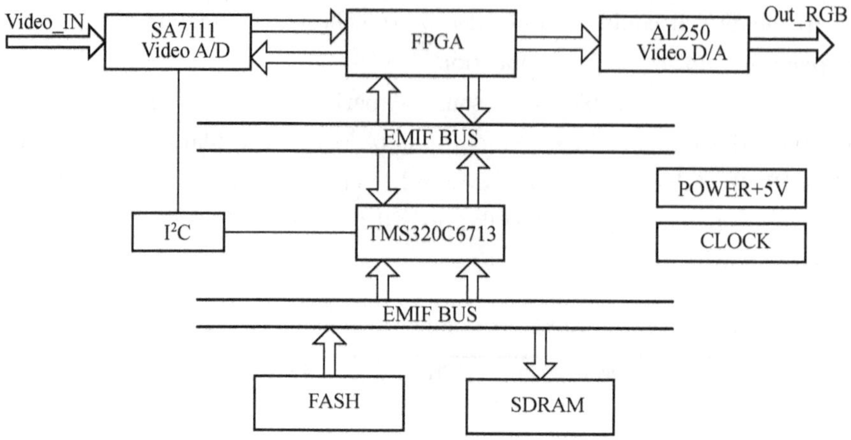

Fig. 4.9. Framework of the DSP platform for the ISRCCBP

and after the C-codes optimization for functions of the irregular region segmentation-IRSPCNN( ) and reconstructing image-RI( ), indicating the importance of optimization.

Table 4.6. Comparison of executing efficiency

Functions	Before(cycles)	Time(ms)	After(cycles)	Time(ms)
IRSPCNN()	25943508	115.30	5068328	22.51
RI()	2370606	10.54	834683	3.71

Summary

In this chapter, we mainly explore the irregular segmented region compression coding based on the PCNN. It cannot only obtain the details but also get the higher compression ratio. the ISRCCBP will be more matchable to human visual characteristics. Much interest has been shown in the region encoding for the purpose of the image compression. However, to the best of our knowledge, little or no attention has been given to the irregular segmented region coding based on the PCNN recently. This work may, in fact, represent the first attempt in the image coding research field.

Reference

[1] ISO/IEC 10918-1 (1994) Information technology-digital compression and coding of continuous-tone still images - part 1: requirements and guidelines, February, 1994.

[2] ITU-T (1993) Recommendation H.261, Line transmission of non-telephone signals. Video code for audio visual services at P*64kbit/s, March 1993.sde

[3] ISO/IEC 11172-2 (1993) Information technology-coding of moving pictures and associated audio for digital storage media at up to about 1.5mbit/s - part 2: Video, August, 1993.

[4] ISO/IEC 13818-2 (1994) Information technology-generic coding of moving pictures and associated audio information - part 2: Video, March, 1994.

[5] Kunt M, Ikonomopoulos A, Kocher M (1985) Second generation image-coding techniques. Proceedings of the IEEE 73: 549 – 574

[6] Kunt M, Benard M, Leonardi R (1987) Recent results in high-compression image coding. IEEE Transactions on Circuits and Systems 34(11): 1306 – 1336

[7] Gilge M (1990) Region-oriented transform coding (ROTC) of images. In: IEEE International Conference on Acoustics, Speech, and Signal Processing, Albuquerque, 3 – 6 April 1990

[8] Reid MM, Millar RJ, Black ND (1997) Second-generation image coding: an overview. ACM Computing Surveys 29(1): 3 – 29

[9] Freeman H (1961) On the encoding of arbitrary geometric configurations. IEEE Transactions on Electronic Computers 10(2): 260 – 268

[10] Walsh JL (1965) Interpolation and approximation by rational functions in the complex domain, 4th edn. American Mathematical Society Colloquium Publications, America

[11] Philips W (1992) A fast algorithm for the generation of orthogonal base functions on an arbitrarily shaped region. In: IEEE International Conference on Acoustics, Speech, and Signal Processing, San Francisco, 23 – 26 March 1992.

[12] Johnson JL, Padgett ML (1999) PCNN model and applications. IEEE Transactions on Neural Networks 10(3): 480 – 498

[13] Ma YD, Li L, Dai RL (2002) Automated image segmentation using PCNN and entropy of image. Journal of China Institute of Communications 29(3): 49 – 51

[14] Ma YD, Li L, Dai R L (2001) Image segmentation embryonic plant cell using PCNN. China Science Bulletin 46(21): 1781 – 1788

[15] Lindblad T, Kinser J (1998) Image processing using pulse-coupled neural networks. Springer-Verlag, Sweden

[16] Ma YD, Li L, Zhan K et al (2008) PCNN and digital image processing, 2nd edn. Science Press, Beijing

[17] Ma YD, Shi F, Li L (2003) A new kind of impulse noise filter based on PCNN. In: Proceedings of 2003 International Conference on Neural Networks and Signal Processing, Nanjing, 14 – 17 December 2003

[18] Ma YD, Wang ZB, Wu CH (2006) Feature extraction from noisy images using PCNN. In: The IEEE International Conference on Information Acquisition, Weihai, 20 – 23 August 2006

[19] Su MJ (2009) Image Processing Based on Pulse Coupled Neuron Networks and Its Implementation on DSP. MD Thesis, LanZhou University, Lanzhou, China

Chapter 5 Image Enhancement

Image enhancement is one of the most commonly used methods in the image pre-processing aiming at improving visual effects for a specific purpose. In other words, the region of interest of images will be prominent after the image enhancement for easier analysis by human or computers. However, there exists no general or uniform standard for evaluating the enhancement quality objectively, because image enhancement methods usually depend on the special needs for some particular applications. In most cases, the enhancement effects are evaluated by the visual perception.

As described in the early chapters, the PCNN will be a good image enhancement tool, due to its ability of different operations for different intensity. Particularly, the pixels with a high intensity are processed coarsely, while the pixels with a low intensity are processed accurately. That is consistent with the visual perception of the human visual system, which has a low sensitivity for the high intensity of stimulus, but high sensitivity for the low intensity. So, the PCNN is widely used in the image enhancement.

5.1 Image Enhancement [1 – 5]

Image enhancement approaches fall into two broad categories: spatial domain methods and frequency domain methods [1].

5.1.1 Image Enhancement in Spatial Domain

In the image processing, the term spatial domain refers to the image plane itself, and approaches in this category are based on direct manipulation of pixels of an image [1]. Spatial domain enhancement approaches also fall into two categories: the transformation method and the spatial domain filtering method. The former is based on individual pixels, and the latter is based on neighborhoods.

Spatial Domain Transformation Enhancement

The spatial domain transformation enhancement methods in common use are basic gray level transformation, histogram processing, and arithmetic operations.

(1) Basic gray level transformation enhancement methods mainly include image negatives, log transformations, power-law transformations (PT), contrast-stretching transformation (CST), and piecewise-linear transformation (PLT). Fig. 5.1 shows some examples and histograms of them, and Fig. 5.2 the effects of the CST [2] and PLT.

(2) The histogram processing enhancement methods mainly include the histogram specification and histogram equalization. The histogram specifi-

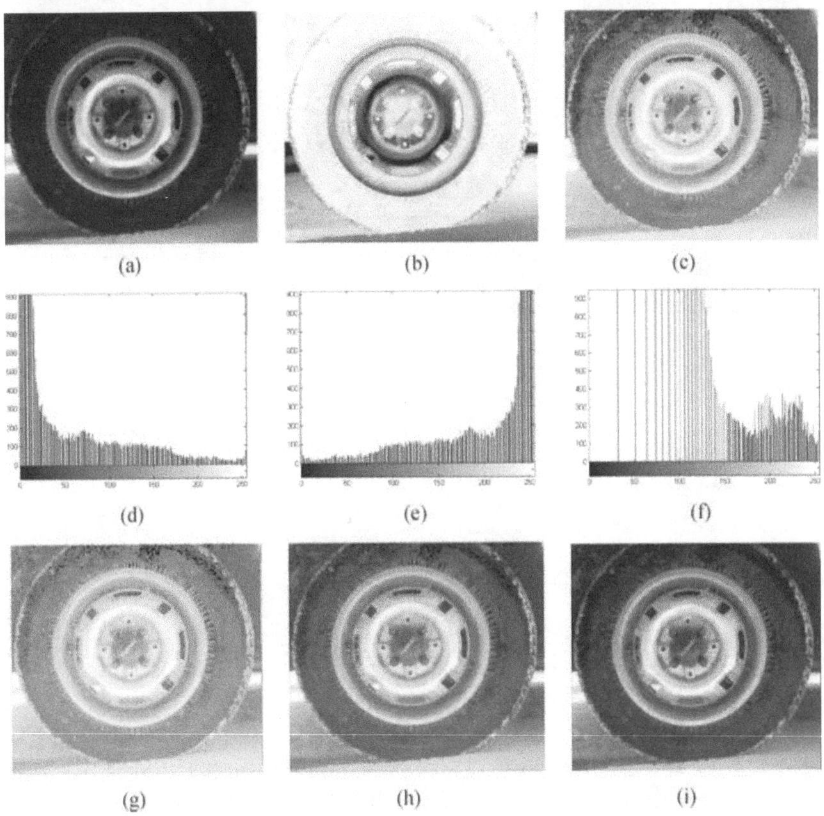

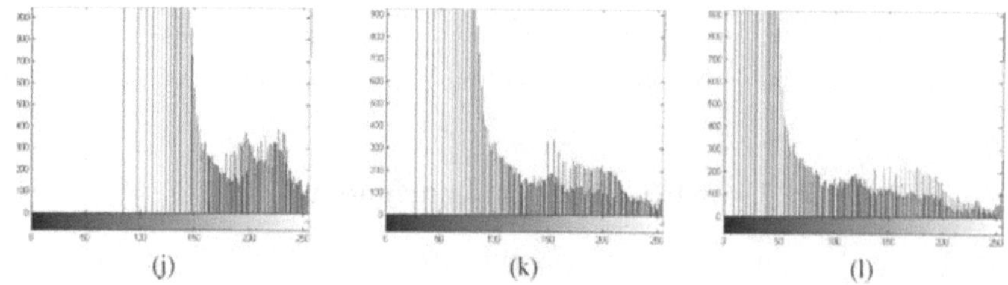

Fig. 5.1. Image negatives, log transformations, and PT results (γ is the value of power). (a) Tire; (b) negatives; (c) log transformations; (d) histogram of (a); (e) histogram of (b); (f) histogram of (c); (g) PT(γ = 0.2); (h) PT(γ = 0.4); (i) PT($\gamma = 0.6$); (j) histogram of (g); (k) histogram of (h); (l) Histogram of (i)

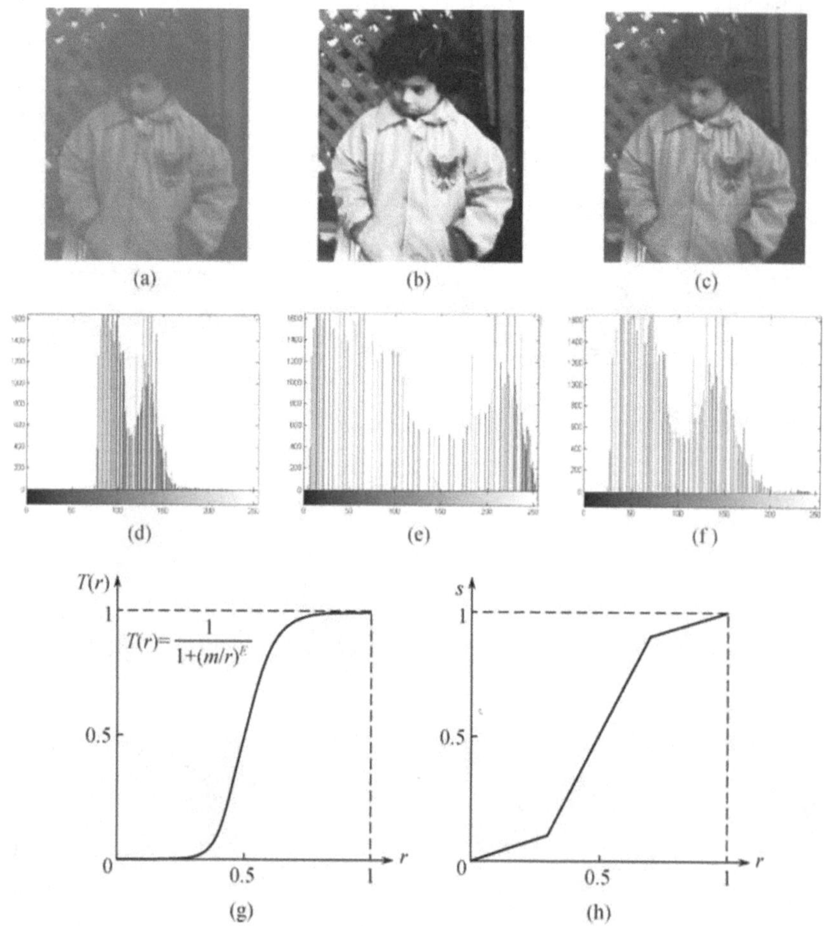

Fig. 5.2. CST and PLT results. (a) Pout; (b) CST(E = 10); (c) PLT; (d) Histogram of (a); (e) Histogram of (b); (f) Histogram of (c); (g) CST function; (h) PLT function

cation is a prior knowledge-based method in that the shape of the wished histogram needs to be designated, while the histogram equalization is a popularly image enhancement method, which will be introduced in Section 5.1.3 of this chapter later.

Spatial Domain Filtering Enhancement

The spatial domain filtering enhancement methods commonly used are smoothing spatial filters and sharpening spatial filters. The mean filter and median filter are some of the widely used smoothing spatial filters, and their enhanced effects are shown in Fig. 5.3. The laplacian filter is a popularly used sharpening spatial filter, and Fig. 5.4 shows its filtered result, which is obtained by subtracting Laplacian filtered image from the original one [2]. Other ways to classify spatial domain filtering enhancement methods are the linear spatial filtering and nonlinear spatial filtering. The Laplacian filtering and the mean filtering belong to the linear spatial filtering while the median filtering belongs to the nonlinear spatial filtering.

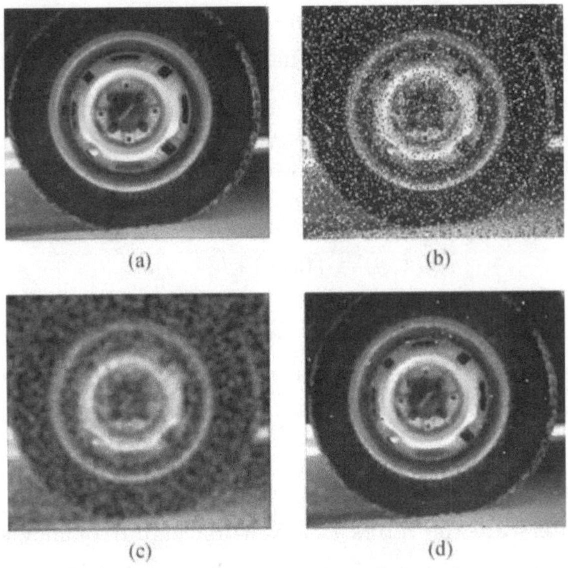

Fig. 5.3. Image mean and median filtering. (a)Tire; (b) Noisy image; (c) mean filtering; (d) median filtering

Fig. 5.4. Laplacian filtering enhancement. (a) Laplacian filtered result; (b) enhanced image

5.1.2 Image Enhancement in Frequency Domain

Frequency domain processing techniques are based on modifying the Fourier transform of an image [1]. Let $f(x, y)$ be the original image and $F(u, v)$ be its Fourier transform, while $h(x, y)$ be a filter and its Fourier transform be $H(u, v)$, and then $f(x, y)$ is transformed to $g(x, y)$ after convolving with $h(x, y)$. And $G(u, v)$ is the Fourier transform of $g(x, y)$. The above procedure can be described in the frequency domain

$$G(u, v) = F(u, v) \cdot H(u, v) \tag{5.1}$$

and in the spatial domain

$$g(x, y) = f(x, y) * h(x, y). \tag{5.2}$$

where "$\cdot$" is multiplication operator and "$*$" means convolution operator. It is known from Eqs. (5.1) – (5.2) that if $h(x, y)$ is chosen correctly, the image $f(x, y)$ will then be effectively enhanced. Brief introductions of several filters are given below.

1) Lowpass filters

Lowpass filters are the filters that restrain high-frequency signals of an image's spectrum and retain the low-frequency signals. Edges and other sharp transitions (such as noises) in the gray levels of an image contribute significantly to the high-frequency components of its Fourier transform. Hence, smoothing is achieved in the frequency domain by lowpass filtering. The ideal lowpass filter, Butterworth lowpass filter, exponential lowpass filter, and trapezoidal lowpass filter are four kinds of lowpass filters commonly used.

2) Highpass filters

The highpass filters are one kind of the filters that restrain low-frequency signals of an image's spectrum and retain the high-frequency signals. As indicated above, edges and other abrupt changes in gray levels are associated with high-frequency components. So, sharpening can be achieved in the frequency domain by highpass filtering. The highpass filters in common use are ideal highpass filter, Butterworth highpass filter, exponential highpass filter, and trapezoidal highpass filter.

3) Band elimination filters and band pass filters

Band elimination filters restrain the middle-frequency signals while retaining high-frequency signals and low-frequency signals. On the contrary, band pass filters restrain high-frequency signals and low-frequency signals while retaining the middle-frequency signals. Usually, these kinds of filters are used to highlight the objectives in a certain range of image spectrums.

Figure 5.5 shows the ideal lowpass filter, Butterworth lowpass filter, ideal highpass filter, and Butterworth highpass filter. Fig. 5.6 gives the results of the Butterworth lowpass filtering and the highpass filtering.

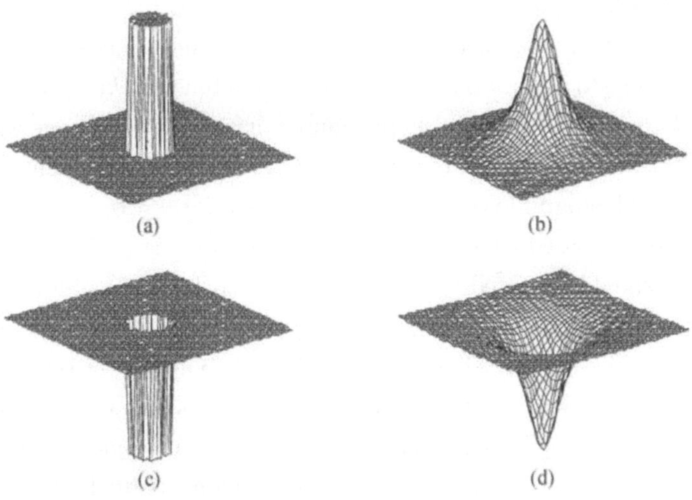

Fig. 5.5. Ideal and Butterworth filters. (a) Ideal lowpass filter; (b) Butterworth lowpass filter; (c) Ideal highpass filter; (d) Butterworth highpass filter

Fig. 5.6. Image frequency filtering. (a) Lena; (b) lowpass filtering result; (c) high-pass filtering result

5.1.3 Histogram Equalization

As mentioned above, there are many different kinds of techniques to enhance an image, among which the histogram equalization is popular one. It belongs to the spatial domain transformation enhancement method.

Histogram of Digital Image

Assume that the gray level of a digital image belongs to the range $[0, L-1]$, and then the histogram of this image is a discrete function $h(r_k) = n_k$, where r_k is the k th gray level and n_k is the number of pixels in the image with gray level r_k. In addition, the total number of pixels in the image is denoted by n. A normalized histogram is given by $p(r_k) = n_k/n$, for $k = 0, 1, ..., L-1$. Here $p(r_k)$ can be regarded as an estimate of the occurrence probability of gray level r_k. It should be noted that the sum of all components of a normalized histogram equals 1.

Histogram images are shown in Figs. 5.7(d), (e), and (f) correspond to Figs. 5.7(a), (b), and (c), respectively. From Fig. 5.7, it can be seen that in the dark image the components of the histogram concentrate on the low side of the gray scale. On the contrary, the components of the histogram of the bright image are biased toward the high side, and the components of the histogram in the high-contrast image cover a broad range of the gray scale. Obviously, an image with low contrast corresponds to a narrow distribution of histogram, while an image with its pixels tending to occupy the entire range of possible gray levels and distributing uniformly will have an appearance of high contrast. That is to say, if the histogram of an image with dark, bright or low contrast is transformed to the histogram that occupies a broad range of possible gray levels and tends to be distributed uniformly, then the image becomes a high contrast one. It is the aim of the histogram equalization.

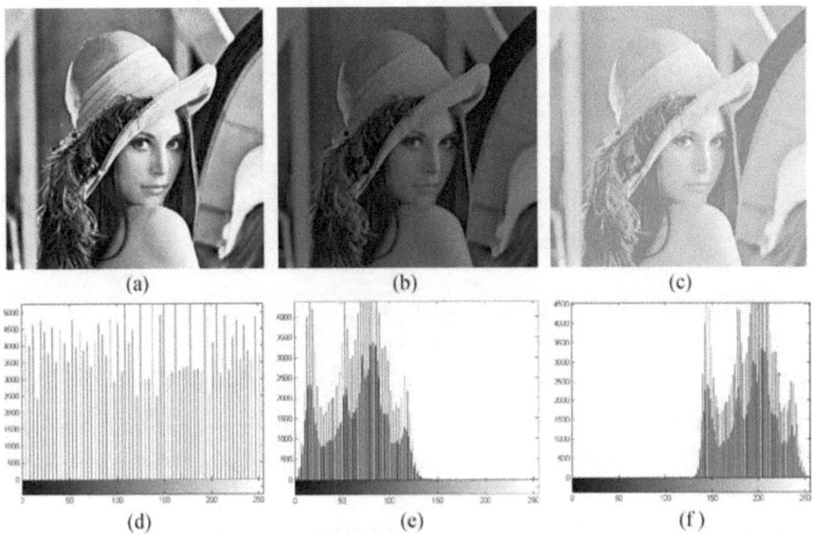

Fig. 5.7. Three basic image types and their corresponding histograms. (a) a high-contrast image; (b) a dark image; (c) a bright image; (d) the histogram of (a); (e) the histogram of (b); (f) the histogram of (c)

Histogram equalization [1]

Histogram equalization is one of methods belonging to the histogram processing or histogram modification.

In a moment continuous function, let the variable r, which has been normalized to the interval [0, 1], represent the gray level of the image to be enhanced where $r = 0$ represents black and $r = 1$ represents white.

Then the transformation is

$$s = T(r) \quad 0 \leqslant r \leqslant 1, \tag{5.3}$$

Eq. (5.3) produces a level s for every pixel value r in the original image. At the same time, the transformation function $T(r)$ is the single-value and monotonically increasing in the interval [0, 1] for any r in [0, 1].

The inverse transformation from s back to r is denoted by

$$r = T^{-1}(s) \quad 0 \leqslant s \leqslant 1. \tag{5.4}$$

Let $p_r(r)$ denote the probability density functions of r and $p_s(s)$ denote the probability density functions of s. The relation between $p_r(r)$ and $p_s(s)$ is

$$p_s(s) = p_r(r)\left|\frac{\mathrm{d}r}{\mathrm{d}s}\right|. \tag{5.5}$$

In order to stretch the contrast of an image, let us try the cumulative distribution function (CDF)

$$s = T(r) = \int_0^r p_r(w)\mathrm{d}w, \tag{5.6}$$

where w is a dummy variable of integration.

So,

$$\frac{\mathrm{d}s}{\mathrm{d}r} = \frac{\mathrm{d}T(r)}{\mathrm{d}r} = \frac{\mathrm{d}}{\mathrm{d}r}\left[\int_0^r p_r(w)\mathrm{d}w\right] = p_r(r). \tag{5.7}$$

Substituting this result for $\mathrm{d}r/\mathrm{d}s$ into Eq. (5.5) yields

$$p_s(s) = p_r(r)\left|\frac{\mathrm{d}r}{\mathrm{d}s}\right| = p_r(r)\left|\frac{1}{p_r(r)}\right| = 1 \quad 0 \leqslant s \leqslant 1. \tag{5.8}$$

So far, it has been demonstrated that performing the transformation function of the CDF can yield a uniform histogram.

For discrete values, the probability of the occurrence of gray level r_k in an image is approximated by

$$p_r(r_k) = \frac{n_k}{n} \quad k = 0, 1, 2, ..., L-1, \tag{5.9}$$

where n is the total number of pixels in the image, n_k is the number of pixels with gray level r_k, and L is the total number of possible gray levels in the image. The discrete version of CDF is

$$s_k = T(r_k) = \sum_{j=0}^{k} p_r(r_j) = \sum_{j=0}^{k} \frac{n_j}{n} \quad k = 0, 1, 2, ..., L-1. \tag{5.10}$$

(a) (b)

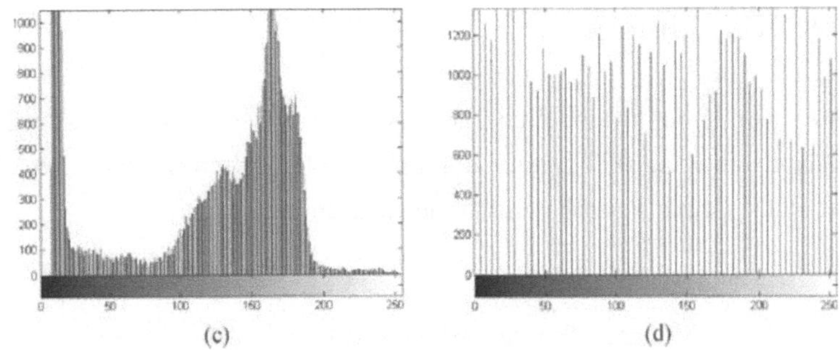

Fig. 5.8. Histogram equalization for cameraman. (a) Cameraman; (b) result of histogram equalization; (c) histogram of (a); (d) histogram of (b)

Finally, after the transformation with Eq. (5.10), the histogram equalized image will be obtained. For more details about histogram equalization, one can refer to Ref.[1]. Figs. 5.8 and 5.9 show the significant improvement of histogram equalization.

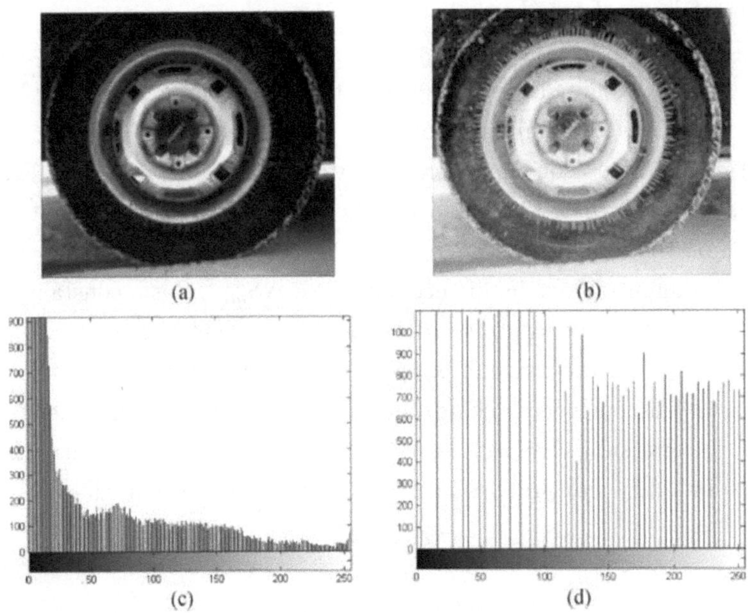

Fig. 5.9. Histogram equalization for Tire. (a) Tire; (b) result of histogram equalization; (c) histogram of (a); (d) histogram of (b)

5.2 PCNN Time Matrix

In this section, human visual characteristics are described firstly. And then the relation between PCNN and human visual characteristics is explained. At last, PCNN time matrix is introduced in detail.

5.2.1 Human Visual Characteristics [6]

Movie, television technology, and developing video processing technology make full use of the human visual characteristic, which is described as follows:

(1) Mach Band Effect, one of the most important features of the human visual system to perceive objects shows that the sensitivity of subjective perception of the human visual system to the luminance difference of the edge is different obviously, where the lower intensity will be darker and the higher intensity will be brighter, especially an intense feeling of contrast in the abrupt jump of gray levels.

(2) The luminance difference, which is subjectively perceived by human visual system, is limited. In other words, the difference, perceived by human vision, is not almost infinitely small.

(3) The response of human vision to gray levels obeys Weber-Fechner law, which shows that the luminance difference, perceived by human vision, depends on the intensity itself. In detail, for any intensity with the value of S, the minimum relative luminance difference $\Delta S_{min}/S$ is a constant ξ (the sensitivity threshold of contrast or Weber-Fechner coefficient).

Usually ξ is in the range of 0.005 to 0.02, and it increases to 0.05 when the intensity becomes too high or too low. Furthermore, the increment of the magnitude of a subjective sensation is not proportional to the increment of physical intensity, but proportional to the relative increment, that is

$$\Delta I = \Delta S/S. \tag{5.11}$$

Applying the integral operation to both side $\Delta S/S$ of Eq. (5.11) can produces

$$I = klnS + r, \tag{5.12}$$

where k and r are constants. Eq. (5.12) clearly demonstrates that the magnitude of a subjective sensation I has the linear relation to the logarithm of the stimulus intensity S, that is the logarithmic model of human visual perception. After hundreds of millions of years of evolution, the human visual system has become adaptive to the variation of luminance to keep out the harmful stimulus of light.

(4) The persistence of vision or duration of vision is another one of the most important features of human visual system to perceive objects.

The response of human vision does not produce a feeling of stable luminance immediately when a certain amount of illumination stimulus acts on the retina. That is to say, it needs a process of transient variation to obtain a stable feeling of intensity. On the other side, the subjective feeling of luminance response decreases gradually rather than sharply fall down to zero when the light disappears immediately. This response lasts about 0.02 s in the day time, and about 0.2 s in the night, and the difference between them is about 0.1 s. The former shows that the perception of human vision lags behind the objective luminance variation and the latter shows the persistence of vision.

The response of human vision is not uniform for all frequencies of luminance changes. And the persistence of vision makes the human vision capable of perceiving the light pulses with frequencies lower than a certain threshold frequency (the critical frequency) 48 Hz, and not capable of perceiving the stimulus with frequencies of light pulses higher than that threshold frequency, but these stimuli with higher frequencies will produce visual fatigue after long time.

In movies and television broadcast, the critical frequency is used for producing the feeling of continuous movement, and human vision perceives the vision consisting of the average intensity of the pictures.

5.2.2 PCNN and Human Visual Characteristics

The PCNN is a quantificational description of the signal transduction property of the neurons in the mammalian visual cortex, so it further reveals the important property of the human visual system. This can be inferred from Chapter 1.

(1) The synchronous oscillation of impulses activated by the PCNN neurons and the capture property demonstrates the limitation of human vision

in perceiving the luminance variation, that is to say, the luminance difference of two kinds of intensity which is lower than a minimum limited constant is difficult to distinguish. It is the principle of regional segmentation.

(2) Neurons of the PCNN, which are described with leakage integrators, correspond to pixels in an image and their stimuli correspond to the intensity.

(3) The performance of the dynamic threshold which attenuates with exponent in PCNN demonstrates that the next firing is not immediately activated after the previous firing until the threshold decreases to a value near the present intensity of internal activity.

(2) and (3) correspond to the phenomenon of lagging on detecting luminance variation and the feature of exponential attenuation in the persistence of vision.

In brief, (1), (2), and (3) imply that PCNN model includes many human visual characteristics.

The exponential attenuation of dynamic threshold (E) shown in Fig. 5.10 demonstrates that the neurons with lower gray levels fire much later than neurons with higher gray levels, which accords with the uneven perception of human vision to different intensity.

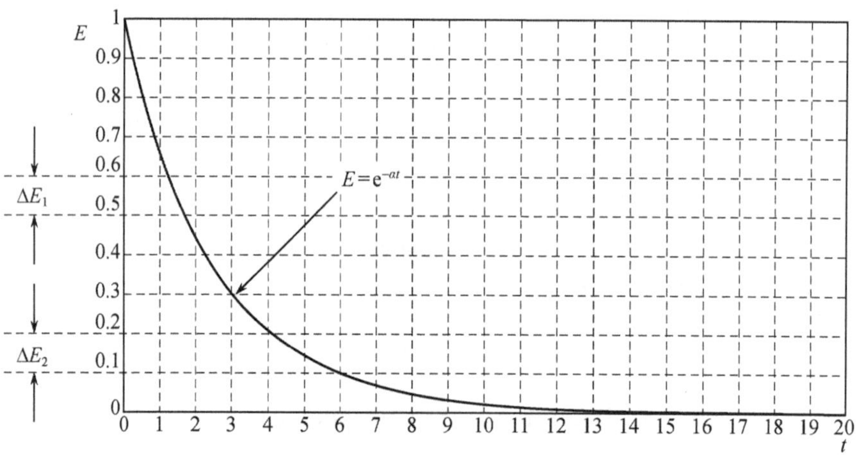

Fig. 5.10. Threshold exponential attenuation curve

In addition, it can also be seen that the same contrast variation in different backgrounds corresponds to different firing time moments, for example, for the same gray level variation ΔE_1 and ΔE_2, the neuron fires earlier on the larger gray level background than that on the lower gray level background.

In other words, the response of the higher gray levels is smaller than the lower gray levels and the response of the contrast variation in brighter background is smaller than the one in darker background.

Finally, the contrast variation of higher intensity is processed coarsely, while the one of lower intensity is processed accurately.

5.2.3 PCNN Time Matrix [7]

Time matrix of the PCNN, described in Chapter 2, is defined to record the first iteration time for all of the neurons. If the internal activity is equal to stimulus, by assumption, from Eq. (1.19) in Chapter 1, the time matrix

$$T = n_1 = \frac{1}{\alpha_E} \ln\left(\frac{E_{ij}(0)}{U_{ij}(n_1)}\right) \approx \frac{1}{\alpha_E} \ln\left(\frac{E_{ij}(0)}{S_{ij}}\right). \tag{5.13}$$

So,

$$\ln S = -\alpha_E T + \ln E(0). \tag{5.14}$$

Comparing Eq. (5.14) with Eq. (5.12), if we assume the time matrix as the perceived intensity of the stimuli and the input of the PCNN as physical magnitudes of stimuli, we could conclude that the relation between T and S in Eq. (5.14), which is the logarithmic rule, is the same as the relation between I and S in Eq. (5.12). Therefore, Eq. (5.14) incarnates Weber-Fechner Law.

In fact, the time matrix is a mapping from the spatial image information to the time information, which gives a genuine record of the information about the firing time moment of each neuron. Obviously, it obeys the Weber-Fechner Law which is the main property of the human visual system. A small value in T indicates that the corresponding pixel has a great intensity, so it belongs to a brighter region. On the contrary, a big value in T indicates that the corresponding pixel has a low intensity, so it belongs to a darker region. The pixels with higher intensity are processed coarsely, while the pixels with lower intensity are processed accurately, which has been explained above.

Put Eq. (5.14) into Eq. (5.12), then the enhanced image, I is

$$I = k(-\alpha_E T + \ln E(0)) + r = -k'T + r'. \tag{5.15}$$

Equation (5.15) describes the link between the perceived intensity of the stimuli and the time matrix of the PCNN.

The enhanced image will be obtained by the reversing of T according to Eq. (5.15).

5.3 Modified PCNN Model [7]

For image enhancement, we modify the PCNN model as follows. The output time matrix is the enhanced image of the original one.

$$F_{ij}(n) = \mathrm{e}^{-\alpha_F} F_{ij}(n-1) + V_F \sum_{kl} W_{ijkl} Y_{kl}(n-1) + S_{ij}. \tag{5.16}$$

$$L_{ij}(n) = \mathrm{e}^{-\alpha_L} L_{ij}(n-1) + V_L \sum_{kl} M_{ijkl} Y_{kl}(n-1). \tag{5.17}$$

$$U_{ij}(n) = F_{ij}(n)(1 + \beta L_{ij}(n)). \tag{5.18}$$

$$E_{ij}(n) = \mathrm{e}^{-\alpha_E} E_{ij}(n-1). \tag{5.19}$$

$$Y_{ij}(n) = \begin{cases} 1 & U_{ij}(n) > E_{ij}(n), \\ 0 & \text{Otherwise.} \end{cases} \tag{5.20}$$

$$T_{ij}(n) = \begin{cases} n & Y_{ij}(n) = 1, Mark_{ij}(n) = 0, \\ 0 & \text{Otherwise.} \end{cases} \tag{5.21}$$

$$Mark_{ij}(n) = \begin{cases} \infty & Y_{ij}(n) = 1, \\ 0 & \text{Otherwise.} \end{cases} \tag{5.22}$$

$$E_{ij}(n) = \begin{cases} \infty & Y_{ij}(n) = 1, \\ E_{ij}(n) & \text{Otherwise.} \end{cases} \tag{5.23}$$

It can be seen from Eq. (5.19) that the dynamic threshold, E, changed obviously. The reason why the term $V_E Y(n-1)$ doesn't appear here is that time matrix records only the first firing time, and $V_E Y(n-1)$ can be expressed by Eq. (5.22). In addition, a term of enhanced image, T, appears in the modified model.

5.4 Image Enhancement Using PCNN Time Matrix [7]

The enhanced image I, which derives from Eq. (5.15), will be the negative time matrix of the modified PCNN model, in which the iteration stops when all neurons have been fired.

Cameraman, tire, and pout are processed by modified PCNN, and the results are shown in Fig. 5.11 – Fig. 5.13. In the histogram equalization, several gray levels are merged into one level after the gray level approximation, which causes the decrease of the number of gray levels, and this can be seen from the contrast distortion of Figs. 5.11(b), 5.12(b), and 5.13(b).

Figs. 5.11(c), (d) tell us that with the stretch of the contrast in the lower intensity, the contrast in the higher part decreases. It is well proved by the results of tire, but its effects are not as apparent as in pout for lack of lower and higher intensity in Fig. 5.13 (d).

In Figs. 5.11 (e), (f), the contrast of coat and buildings is much lower than the original image. These two methods increase the contrast of middle section of the gray scale at the expense of the contrast of the lower and higher sections

(a) (b)

(c) (d)

(e) (f)

(g)

(h)

Fig. 5.11. Comparison between modified PCNN and other methods using cameraman. (a) Cameraman; (b) histogram equalization; (c) log transformations; (d) PT ($\gamma = 0.4$); (e) CST (E = 10); (f) PLT; (g) enhanced by Laplacian filter; (h) modified PCNN

which can be seen in Figs. 5.2(g), (h). Figs. 5.12 (e), (f) show the same results. The distribution of the histogram of pout (Fig. 5.2(d)) concentrates on the middle section, so contrast of the lower and higher intensity, seen in Figs. 5.13(e), (f), has not changed obviously.

The Laplacian filtering enhancement method shown in cameraman, tire, and pout only improves the edge information, while the overall contrast of intensity has not been stretched apparently.

(a)

(b)

(c)

(d)

Fig. 5.12. Comparison between the modified PCNN and other methods using tire, (a) Tire; (b) Histogram equalization; (c) Log transformations; (d) PT ($\gamma = 0.4$); (e) CST ($E = 10$); (f) PLT; (g) Enhanced by Laplacian filter; (h) Modified PCNN

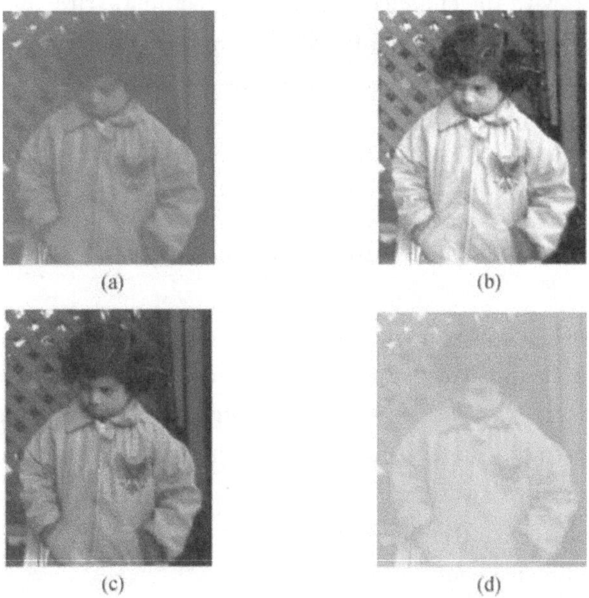

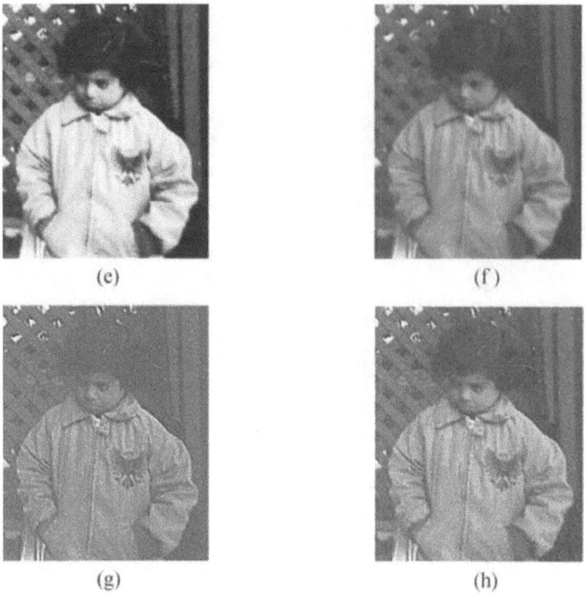

Fig. 5.13. Comparison between the modified PCNN and other methods using pout. (a) Pout; (b) Histogram equalization; (c) Log transformations; (d) PT ($\gamma = 0.4$); (e) CST ($E = 10$); (f) PLT; (g) Enhanced by Laplacian filter; (h) Modified PCNN

Compared with the enhanced results of cameraman, tire, and pout, image enhancement method with the PCNN time matrix performs better in Figs. 5.11(h), 5.12(h), and 5.13(h) not only in the overall visual effects but also in the local details and edges.

5.5 Color Image Enhancement Using PCNN

Compared with the gray image, color image carries more information. Color image enhancement is very important to biomedical image processing, particularly with respect to studies of biological growth and development, pathology imaging studies and disease diagnosis using imaging. For example, the images in digital gastrointestinal endoscopy, color ultrasound, surgical operations controlled with computer, etc. depend on digital image processing and color image enhancement.

Different color spaces are used in different occasions, such as the RGB model is used principally in image pickup, monitor, and video processing, the CMY model in color printer, the YIQ model in color video transmission, the HSV model and the HIS model, among which the HIS model is usually used in the special processing of color and is more suitable to the study of the human visual system.

Ref. [5] clearly describes the scheme of color image enhancement with the RGB model. Each of the three channels is processed respectively as a gray level image after coordinate transformation. Finally, the result is obtained by synthesizing all the three channels. According to this idea, the PCNN can be applied to either all the three channels for the gray enhancement or only one channel depending on actual needs. Ref. [8] presents a multi-scale color image enhancement algorithm based on the human visual system using the HSV model. Ref. [9] suggests a fuzzy model for morphological color image processing based on the HSV model, which achieves noise reduction and at the same time remains the details unaffected. Based on Refs. [8,10,11], Ref. [12] applies the principle of the PCNN gray enhancement to the HIS model and presents a color image enhancement method with the PCNN, and its color image enhancement is finished by γ adjustment to the saturation component S and keeps the hue unchanged.

Figures 5.11– 5.13 show the result of gray image processing using the algorithm introduced in Ref. [7]. Now the same algorithm is applied to color image processing, because the HIS model is more suitable to the human visual system. Thus the RGB space is transformed into the HIS space for processing.

Fig. 5.14. The result of color image enhancement using PCNN [7]. (a) Original image; (b) Enhanced image

For the same hue, the human vision is more sensitive to variations of the luminance than to variations of the color saturation, so combining with the property of the HIS model, the method proposed here uses the PCNN to improve the contrast and dynamic range of the whole image by enhancing the luminance components, and to improve the clarity of the colors with nonlinear adjustment of the saturation component. Because of the sensitivity of the human eyes to hue component H, the original H component should be kept unchanged, which will reduce the computational cost. Similar to Ref. [8, 12], the color image enhancement is achieved by γ adjustment to the saturation component S and the gray enhancement of intensity component I is implemented using the PCNN time matrix. It can be seen from Figs. 5.14 that not only the overall visual clarity but also the local details and contours are effectively enhanced.

Summary

The negative time matrix of PCNN conforms the human subjective perception of stimulus. The human visual perception is much considered in the enhancement algorithm using the PCNN. So, this kind of algorithms has obvious advantages in the image enhancement.

Reference

[1] Gonzales RC, Woods RE (2002) Digital image processing, 2nd edn. Prentice Hall, Upper Saddle River, NJ.

[2] Gonzales RC, Woods RE, Eddins SL (2004) Digital image processing Using MATLAB. Prentice Hall, Upper Saddle River, NJ.

[3] Zhang YJ (1999) Image engineering. Tsinghua University Press, Beijing

[4] Li BC, Peng TQ, Peng B (2004) Intelligent image processing technology. Publishing house of electronics industry, Beijing

[5] Jain AK (1989) Fundamentals of Digital Image Processing. Prentice-Hall, Inc, New Jersey

[6] Yu SL, Guo FY, Li GL et al (1994) Television principle. National Defense Industry Press, Beijing

[7] Zhan K, Zhang HJ, Ma YD (2009) New spiking cortical model for invariant texture retrieval. IEEE Transactions on Neural Networks 20(12): 1980 – 1986

[8] Huang KQ, Wang Q, Wu ZY et al (2003) Multi-scale color image enhancement algorithm based on Human Visual System (HVS). Journal of Image and Graphics 8(11): 1242 – 1246

[9] Ma YD, Yang M (2006) A new kind of fuzzy model for soft morphological color image processing. Journal of Circuits and Systems 11(3): 30 – 35

[10] Zhang JY, Lu T (2003) Enhancement of image by PCNN. Computer Engineering and Applications 1(19): 93–95

[11] Shi MH, Zhang JY, Li YG et al (2005) A new method of low contrast image enhancement. Application Research of Computers 1(1): 235–238

[12] Shi MH, Li YG, Zhang JY et al (2004) Novel method of color image enhancement. Computer Applications 24(10): 69–74

Chapter 6 Image Fusion

The PCNN is a biologically inspired neural network, widely applied in the field of image processing such as the image segmentation, image enhancement, and pattern recognition. This chapter will describe its application in image fusion. Firstly, it will briefly review the development of the image fusion based on the PCNN, and then simply introduce some medical image fusion methods [1]. Finally, it will describe a new method of the multi-focus image fusion suggested in Ref. [2].

6.1 PCNN and Image Fusion

First of all, the foundation of the image fusion, including its definition, hierarchical division and application fields, is briefly reviewed. And then the development of the PCNN in the field of the image fusion is explained.

6.1.1 Preliminary of Image Fusion

The image fusion is an important branch of data fusion that refers to the process of combining data from different sources together so that the fused data provide the most detailed and reliable information as far as possible. Therefore, the image fusion is usually defined as the process of combining relevant information from two or more images into a single image, also known as the fused image. Undoubtedly, the fused image will be more informative than any of the input images [3].

Therefore, the fused image has many advantages: (a) It contains more complete and accurate information; (b) It has higher reliability and robustness; (c) It is easier to be understood by user and computer.

The image fusion is generally divided into three levels: pixel-level fusion, feature-level fusion, and decision-level fusion. The difference of these three levels is that they have different objects of study. Pixel-level fusion belongs to low-level fusion which is the foundation of the others. Pixel-level fusion directly computes the final value of every pixel from input images based on some rules.

Until now the image fusion technique has been widely applied into many fields such as the defense industry, robot vision, digital camera application (e.g., multi-focus image fusion), medical imaging, and satellite image(e.g., remote sensing image).

6.1.2 Applications in Image Fusion

Speaking of the image fusion method, people tend to think of wavelet or pyramid algorithm [4−11], because these methods are usually used to fuse object images. However, the PCNN has a potential ability of the image fusion in its own way. For instance, as early as 1998, Kinser had used this ability to study the spiral image fusion [12]. He proposed the PCNN-based spiral image fusion system and employed inter-channel autowave communication to combine the information from the different channels.

Subsequently, many approaches about the image fusion based on the PCNN have been published in different journals or proceedings. Generally, these PCNN-based algorithms can be divided into two groups.

One is to fuse images together with other methods (e.g., wavelet theory). For example, Broussard et al., firstly segmented the image with the PCNN and then the segmented feature objects and the original image were fused to improve the rate of object recognition [13]. Blasch segmented image, extracted and linked spatial features based on the PCNN, then fused current and learned information with the belied filter [14]. Xu and Chen decomposed the image via the multi-scale contrast pyramid, and subsequently utilized the global coupling property and the synchronous pulse burst property of the PCNN to select the best contrast component from original images [15]. Similarly, Li and Zhu used wavelet packet to decompose the original images into a series of frequency components, and then employed the PCNN to make the decision for choice of fusing frequency components [16]. The other is to only use the PCNN to finish the whole task of the image fusion. Zhang and Liang designed a parallel image fusion system only using a master PCNN and some assistant PCNNs [17]. Li and Tan proposed a region-based image fusion of the PCNN [18]. Firstly, the input image was segmented into different regions, and then the fusion weight coefficient was determined according to the values of salience [18] and visibility [18] of each region, reflecting its clarity. The above schemes have a common trait: they have to run more than one PCNN in parallel. Different from them, Wang and Ma presented a method of image fusion with a single modified PCNN and applied it into medical image fusion [1, 2]. For multi-focus image fusion, Miao and Wang designed an adaptive image fusion algorithm via automatic change of the linking coefficient [19]. Huang and Jing decomposed source image into blocks and reconstructed the final fused image by selecting the image blocks from the source images based on the comparison of the outputs of the PCNN [20].

6.2 Medical Image Fusion

Medical image fusion not only is useful in diagnosing diseases, but also reduces the storage cost by a single fused image instead of multiple source images. Many approaches, such as FSD pyramid [4], gradient pyramid [5], Laplacian pyramid [6], DWT pyramid [7], SIDWT pyramid [8], morphological pyramid [9], ratio pyramid [10], and contrast pyramid [11], have been proposed. Until now, there is not any general method suitable for all kinds of applications, each method is only efficient for specific types of images and each has its own limits. For example, the contrast pyramid method loses too much information in the source images during the process of fusion; the ratio pyramid method produces lots of false information that does not exist in the source images; and morphological pyramid method creates many bad edges. In a word, these methods cannot deal with various types of medical images. In this chapter, another method of the medical image fusion based on a modified model of the PCNN, that is, the multiple-image fusion with the m-PCNN, is described in detail.

6.2.1 Description of Model

In fact, only one stimulus for each neuron is an obstacle for the multiple-image fusion with the basic PCNN. Here, a new fusion method, which is based on the m-PCNN model, is suggested and its expressions have been described in Chapter 1, as shown in Fig. 6.1. Like the original PCNN neuron, each m-PCNN neuron also consists of three parts: dendritic tree, information fusion, and pulse generator. The role of the dendritic tree is to receive two kinds of inputs. The one is from the external stimulus and the other is from the surrounding neurons. The task of the information fusion part is to fuse all data from dendrite tree part. The role of the pulse generator is to generate the output pulse.

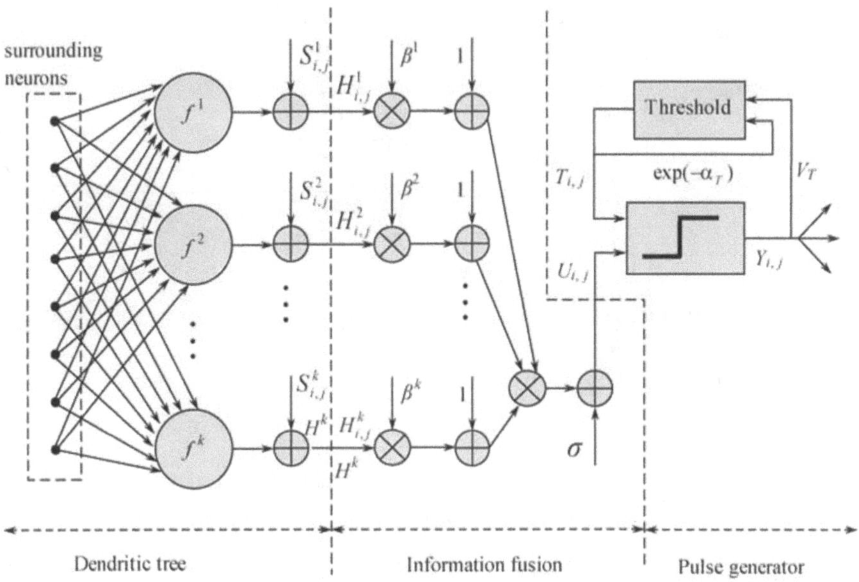

Fig. 6.1. The neuromime of the m-PCNN

When used in the image fusion, the m-PCNN is a single layer two-dimensional array of laterally linked neurons and all neurons are identical. The number of neurons in the network is equal to the number of pixels in each input image. The gray value of a pixel is taken as the stimulus of the neuron. For the same neuron, its stimuli come from the gray value of its corresponding pixels in different images, which have the same position. The data fusion is finished in the interior activation of the neuron by means of internal activity. Note that external input images must be registered and all inputs should also have the identical resolution.

Using one m-PCNN can fuse multiple-source images. Multiple external stimuli work in a neuron at the same time, which makes multiple images processed in a parallel way and less time-consuming in the process of image fusion and cuts down computational complexity as well.

6.2.2 Image Fusion Algorithm

The m-PCNN makes the process of image fusion very simple and efficient. The algorithm is implemented via Fig. 6.2 and described in detail as follows:

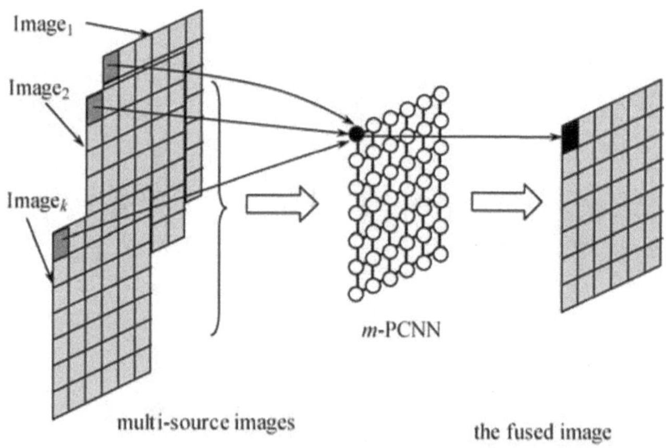

Fig. 6.2. The scheme of the m-PCNN image fusion algorithm

(1) Multi-source images are taken as multiple stimuli of the m-PCNN. Let I^k denotes multi-source images, generally $k > 1$. Namely, $S^k = I^k$. Note that all external input images must be registered and also have the same size and identical resolution.

(2) The stimuli and feed information are transmitted into the neuron via their different channels.

(3) All received signals are mixed together in the internal activity of the neuron. From Eq. (1.27), there are not only linear operations but also non-linear operations in the process of data fusion.

(4) The pulse generator determines the firing events according to the

current threshold. The parameter C_n is used to record the number of the fired neurons at the current iteration. Note that each neuron only fires once in the whole process.

(5) Make $Sum = Sum' + C_n$, where Sum denotes the total number of the fired neurons after the current iteration. Sum' denotes the total number of the fired neurons before the current iteration.

(6) If $Sum < Num$, turn to (2); otherwise, continue. Num means the total number of all neurons in the network.

(7) Normalize the internal state U. The normalized U is the fused image.

Because data fusion happens in the internal activity, the internal state U includes all information needed by fusion. But U could not be directly taken as the final output image, because some values of U may be beyond the value of the dynamic range of the image, it is necessary to adjust U by the linear transformation.

6.2.3 Experimental Results and Analysis

In the experiments, the m-PCNN is taken to fuse different medical images, and its parameters are set empirically as follows:

Table 6.1. Parameters of the m-PCNN in the experiment.

parameters	m	β^1	β^2	σ	α_T	V_T
value	2	0.5	0.5	1.0	0.012	4000

Its convolution core

$$K = \begin{bmatrix} 0.1091, & 0.1409, & 0.1091 \\ 0.1409, & 0, & 0.1409 \\ 0.1091, & 0.1409, & 0.1091 \end{bmatrix}$$

and $M(\cdot) = W(\cdot) = Y[n-1] \otimes K$, where $\otimes$ denotes convolution operation.

As shown in Figs. 6.3–6.6, corresponding to groups 1–4, the first two images are used as the experiment images. Figs. 6.3(a) and (b) come from internet [21], Figs. 6.4(a) and (b) come from Ref. [22]. Figs. 6.5(a) and (b), Figs. 6.6(a) and (b) the come from the website of the Atlas project (which is made possible in part by the Departments of Radiology and Neurology at Brigham and Women's Hospital), Harvard Medical School, the Countway Library of Medicine, and the American Academy of Neurology [23].

In order to evaluate the performance of the algorithm, it is compared with other methods: contrast pyramid, FSD pyramid, gradient pyramid, Laplacian pyramid, morphological pyramid, ratio pyramid, SIDWT with Harr, and DWT with DBSS (2, 2). In the experimental images for groups 1 – 2, Figs. 6.3(a) and (b) and Figs. 6.4(a) and (b) are source images. Figs. 6.3(c) and 6.4(c) are the fused images, the output of the m-PCNN algorithm.

The subsequent images, Figs. 6.3(d) – (i) and Figs. 6.4(d) – (i), are fused by various pyramid algorithms.

The next images, Figs. 6.3(j), (k) and Figs. 6.4(j), (k) are mixed by wavelet transform. Image (j) is obtained by the approach of shift invariant discrete wave transform (SIDWT) with Harr. Image (k) is fused by discrete wavelet transform (DWT), and wavelet is the DBSS (2, 2).

Parameters of these two methods are set by:

pyramid level = 4,

selection rules: highpass = max,

lowpass = average.

The last two images, Figs. 6.3(l) and 6.4(l) are obtained by calculating the average of source images.

In fact, the image fusion is to fuse a variety of multi-source images together and creates a fused image that acquires as much information from each of the source images as possible. The more information obtained from source images, the better the effect of fusion is. The mutual information is used as the objective standard to estimate the performance of different methods included here. It can measure the similarity between two original images. If these two images are more similar, the value of mutual information is larger. Therefore, mutual information will be able to measure the performance of different methods.

In Figs. (6.7) – (6.10), MI_AF denotes mutual information between image A and the fused image F; it is calculated according to Eq. (6.1).

$$\text{MI\_AF} = H(A) + H(F) - H(A, F), \tag{6.1}$$

where $H(A,\ F)$ is joint entropy,

$$H(A, F) = -\sum p(A, F) \log p(A, F), \tag{6.2}$$

MI_BF denotes the mutual information between image B and the fused image F; MI_AB denotes the cumulative mutual information which is the sum of

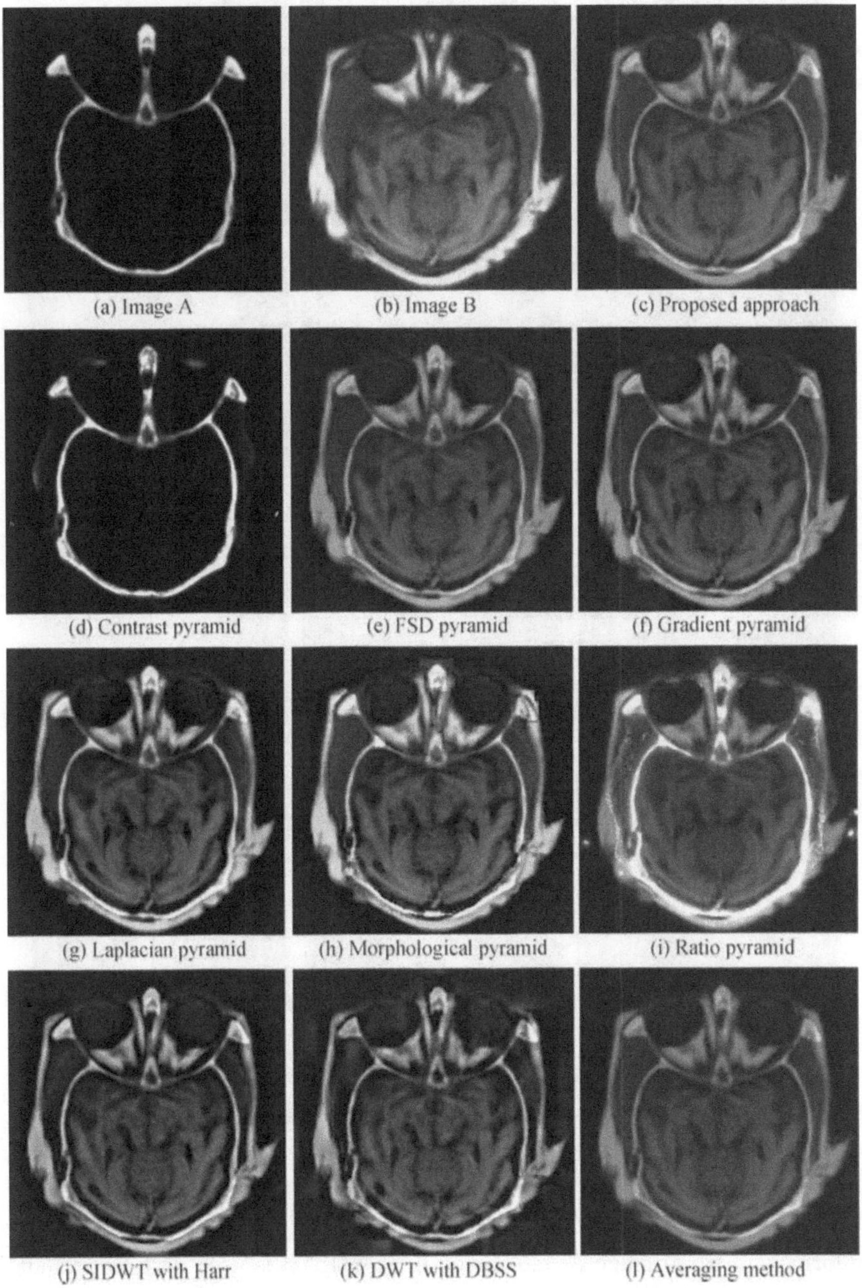

Fig. 6.3. Group 1 experimental images: (a) and (b) are original images; (c) – (l) are fused images

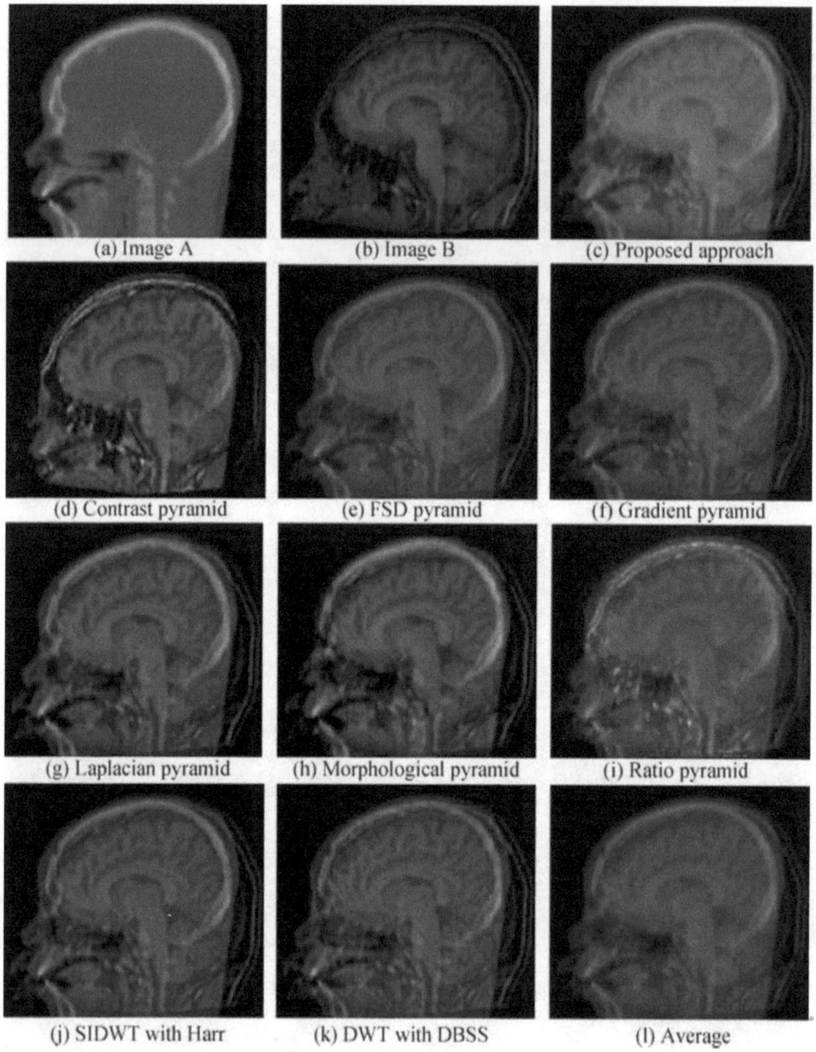

Fig. 6.4. Group 2 experimental images: (a) and (b) are original images; (c) – (l) are fused images

MI_AF and MI_BF; MI_AB shows the ability for a fused image to acquire information from image A and image B, so MI_AB is used here to evaluate different image fusion methods. A larger MI_AB indicates that the fused image acquires more information from image A and image B. In other words, the method with a largest MI_AB is superior to others among the various methods.

To show the better performance of the m-PCNN algorithm, several experiments are performed on four groups of 256-level images: Figs. 6.3(a) and (b) – Figs. 6.6(a) and (b). Each group consists of a pair of medical images from different sources. For example, images in Group 1 are acquired from the same position in the brain using different devices. Image A shown in Fig. 6.3(a) is a CT image that shows structures of bone, while Image B shown in Fig. 6.3(b) is an MR image that shows areas of soft tissues.

In clinical diagnosis or some research of pathology, doctors need to observe the position, the shape of both bone and tissue for judging disease or surveying organ's development. So the fused image is widely used in hospitals, which includes as much of the information in A and B as possible.

From Fig. 6.3, it is clearly observed that Fig. 6.3(d) does not contain the information in the image B; Fig. 6.3(i) contains false information that appears as bright spots, which does not exist in Image A or Image B; and Figs. 6.3(g) and (h) have a good contrast, however, investigating Fig. 6.3(h) carefully shows that there are also some sharp edges. Except for these four images, the remaining images look very similar. Three kinds of mutual information of group 1 are shown in Fig. 6.7 (Note, in Figs. 6.7 – 6.10, PA: Proposed approach; CP: Contrast pyramid; FSD: FSD pyramid; GP: Gradient pyramid; LP: Laplacian pyramid; MP: Morphological pyramid; RP: Ratio pyramid; SIDWT: SIDWT with Harr; DWT: DWT with DBSS; AM: Averaging method). Obviously, the proposed algorithm (PA) is superior to others because of its largest cumulative mutual information MI_AB. And the fused image acquires the most information from the image A and image B, then the better one comes to averaging method, the good one comes to morphological pyramid method and the worst one is the pyramid method.

In Group 2, Fig. 6.4(a) is a CT image and Fig. 6.4(b) is an MR image. Fused images are shown in Figs. 6.4(c) – (k). Ratio pyramid method is worse than the others because of so many bright spots in Fig. 6.4(i), which are false information. Also, Fig. 6.4(d) loses much information of edge in the mouth and Fig. 6.4(h) has bad edges. As shown in Fig. 6.8, IM_AB of the fused image with the m-PCNN algorithm is the biggest one, coming up the next is the averaging method, and morphological pyramid method lies in the third place. The last one is DWT with DBSS (2, 2) having the smallest mutual information.

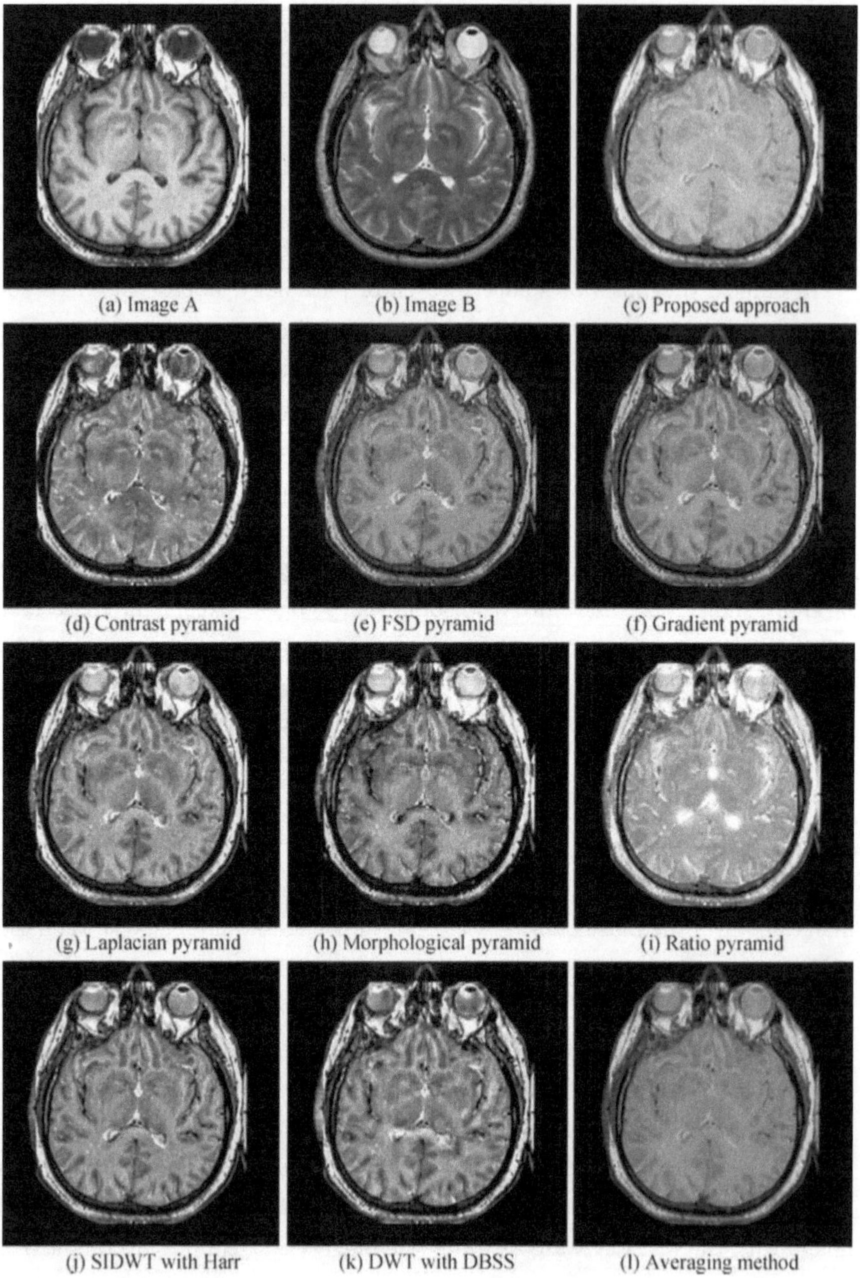

Fig. 6.5. Group 3 experimental images: (a) and (b) are original images; (c) – (l) are fused images

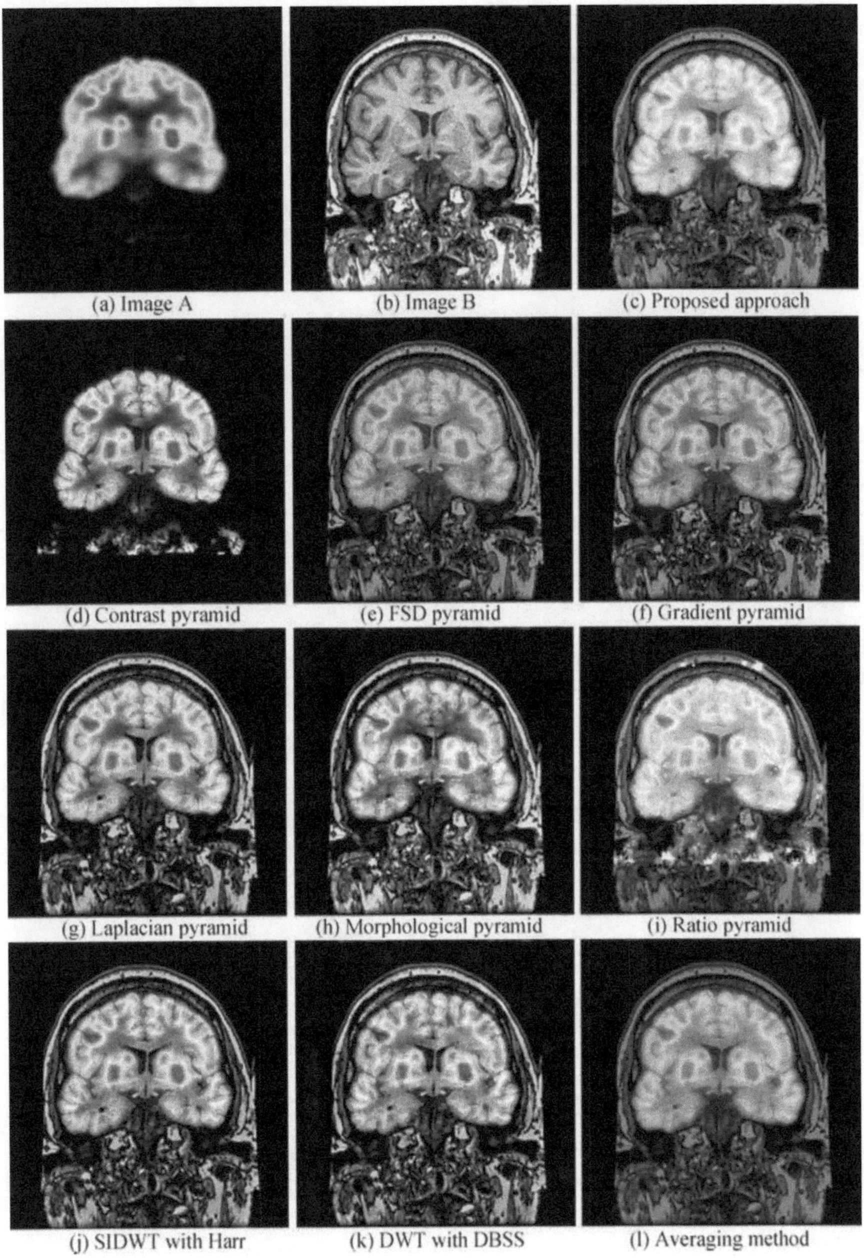

Fig. 6.6. Group 4 experimental images: (a) and (b) are original images, (c) – (l) are fused images

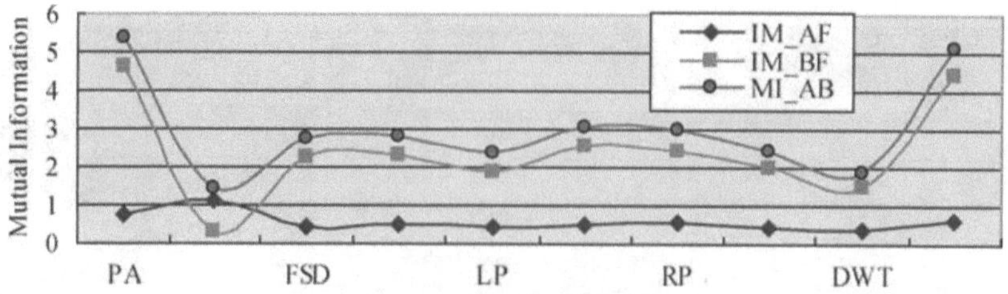

Fig. 6.7. Performance of different methods for Group 1

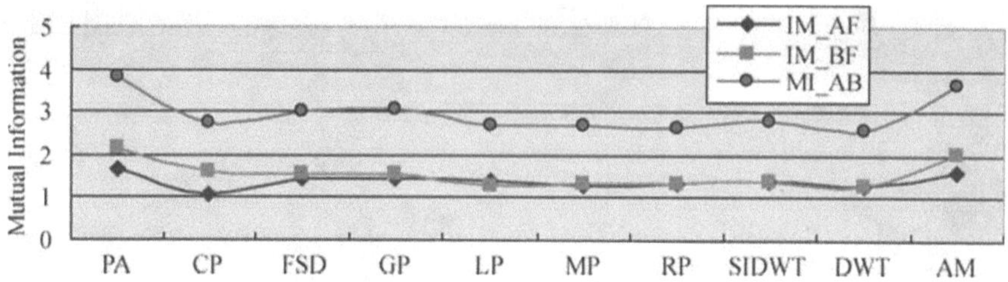

Fig. 6.8. Performance of different methods for Group 2

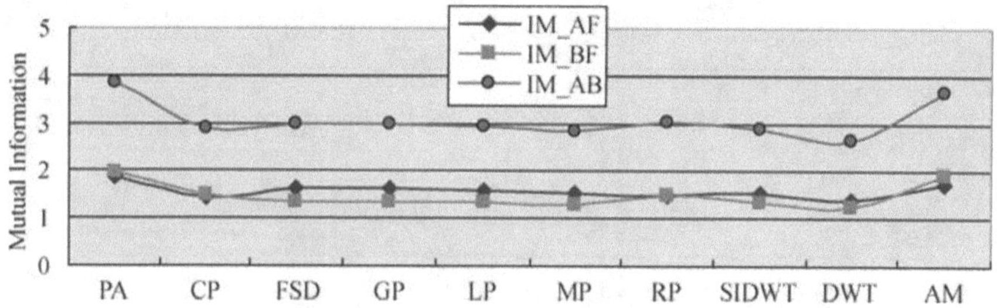

Fig. 6.9. Performance of different methods for Group 3

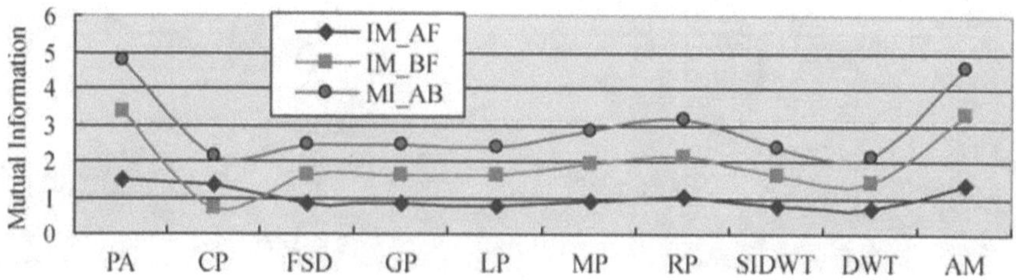

Fig. 6.10. Performance of different methods for Group 4

In Group 3 and Group 4, Fig. 6.5(a), (b) are transaxial brain images. The modality of Fig. 6.5(a) is MR-T1 and the modality of Fig. 6.5(b) is MR-T2. Fig. 6.6(a) is a coronal FDG image and Fig. 6.6(b) is a coronal MR-T1 image.

For Group 3 and Group 4, all the results are shown in Fig. 6.5 and Fig. 6.6. It has been observed clearly that some false edges appear in Fig. 6.5(h) and Fig. 6.6(h) fused with morphological pyramid, and most content of Fig. 6.6(b) is lost in Fig. 6.6(d) fused with contrast pyramid. Obviously, it is the worst result among these included methods.

As shown in Figs. 6.9 and 6.10, in all mutual information of these experiments for all included methods for Group 3 and Group 4, the IM_AB of image fused with the m-PCNN algorithm is the biggest, for these images contain the richest information from source images, and then comes to ratio pyramid method, whereas contrast pyramid method lies in the third place in Figs. 6.7 and 6.8.

According to the mutual information of all included methods, as shown in Figs. 6.7 and 6.10, the fusion performance of others varies depending on different images except the proposed m-PCNN algorithm and averaging method. That means both m-PCNN algorithm and the averaging ones are much more flexible and stable. Nevertheless, the proposed m-PCNN algorithm is always in the first place.

In summary, in the field of the medical image fusion, the proposed m-PCNN algorithm outperforms all other included methods. In addition, it has good flexibility and high stability.

6.3 Multi-focus Image Fusion

The multi-focus image fusion is the process to fuse several images of the same object obtained by different focus settings to produce a new image with extended depth of field, for the purpose of increasing the apparent depth of field. It plays an important role in many different fields such as biomedical imaging and computer vision. The multi-focus image fusion also is one of the main research branches in the field of the image fusion.

Generally, there are two common schemes for the multi-focus image fusion. The one is to use multi-resolution approaches, typically the discrete wavelet transform (DWT) and various pyramid algorithms [4 – 9]. But usually it is complicated and time-consuming and is difficult to implement. The other is based on the selection of image blocks from source images [18, 19]. The idea is to select the better resolution blocks corresponding to the same location in source images to construct the fused image. Clearly, the latter is simpler than the former. However, the latter has some disadvantages. For instance, its fusion effect depends on the focus measurement to a great extent and usually there exist some errors (e.g., misjudgment or wrong selection of image blocks) in the fused image. Therefore, the multi-focus image fusion based on the PCNN was presented [2] and it will be discussed below.

Some multi-focus image fusion algorithms based on PCNN are presented in recent years. However, almost all methods employ more than one PCNN [13, 19] or combine the PCNN with other algorithms such as the DWT [16]. In order to make PCNN more suitable for the image fusion, the m-PCNN is designed and is applied to the multi-focus image fusion so that only one m-PCNN can finish the whole process of the multi-focus image fusion [2].

6.3.1 Dual-channel PCNN

The dual-channel neuron model, derived from the m-PCNN when $m = 2$, also consists of three parts: the dentritic trees, information fusion pool, and the pulse generator. The function of dentritic trees is to receive the stimulus including external inputs and surrounding neurons; information fusion pool is the place where all data are fused; the pulse generator is to generate the output pulse.

There are two input channels corresponding to two stimuli in the dual-channel neuron model. The model is described in the following Eqs. (6.3)–(6.7).

$$H_{ij}^A[n] = S_{ij}^A + \sum_{k,l} w_{ijkl} Y_{kl}[n-1]. \tag{6.3}$$

$$H_{ij}^B[n] = S_{ij}^B + \sum_{k,l} m_{ijkl} Y_{kl}[n-1]. \tag{6.4}$$

$$U_{ij}[n] = (1 + \beta_{ij}^A H_{ij}^A[n])(1 + \beta_{ij}^B H_{ij}^B[n]) + \sigma. \tag{6.5}$$

$$Y_{ij}[n] = \begin{cases} U_{ij}[n] - Sur_{ij}[n] & U_{ij}[n] > E_{ij}[n-1], \\ 0 & \text{Otherwise.} \end{cases} \tag{6.6}$$

$$E_{ij}[n] = \begin{cases} \mathrm{e}^{-\alpha_T} E_{ij}[n-1] & Y_{ij}[n] = 0, \\ V_T & \text{Otherwise.} \end{cases} \tag{6.7}$$

Compared with the basic PCNN, the dual-channel PCNN has a few parameters. In the dual-channel model, instead of the feed channel (F) and the link channel (L), H^A and H^B stand for two symmetrical input channels. β^A and β^B are the weighting coefficients of two symmetrical channels, σ is the level factor to adjust the average level of internal activity. Parameters $(U, E, Y, V_T, w_{ijkl}, m_{ijkl}, \text{and}\alpha_T)$ have the same meanings as these in the basic PCNN model. Sur_{ij} denotes the input from surrounding neurons.

Generally,

$$k_{ijkl} = w_{ijkl} = m_{ijkl}, Sur_{ij} = \sum_{k,l} k_{ijkl} Y_{kl}[n-1].$$

Firstly, two channels of the neuron receive external stimuli and output of surrounding neurons. Furthermore, the data from these channels are weighted and mixed in the information fusion pool according to the weighting coefficients. Finally, the mixed data are released by the neuron as its output with the attenuation of the threshold. The implementation of the dual-channel PCNN is described as follows:

(1) Initialize parameters and matrices. $\boldsymbol{U} = \boldsymbol{O} = \boldsymbol{Y} = 0, \boldsymbol{E} = 1$.

The Initialization of $\boldsymbol{W}$ and $\boldsymbol{M}$ is different from that of other matrices. Here $\boldsymbol{K} = \boldsymbol{W} = \boldsymbol{M}$. Its values are determined empirically.

(2) If $\boldsymbol{S}^A = \boldsymbol{S}^B$, then $\boldsymbol{O} = \boldsymbol{S}^A$ or $\boldsymbol{S}^B$; and go to step (6).

(3) Normalize external stimuli's value in the range: [0, 1].

(4) $\boldsymbol{Sur} = \boldsymbol{Y} \otimes \boldsymbol{K}$;

$\boldsymbol{H}^A = \boldsymbol{S}^A + \boldsymbol{Sur}$;

$\boldsymbol{H}^B = \boldsymbol{S}^B + \boldsymbol{Sur}$;

$\boldsymbol{U} = (1 + \boldsymbol{\beta}^A * \boldsymbol{H}^A)(1 + \boldsymbol{\beta}^B * \boldsymbol{H}^B) + \sigma$.

If $\boldsymbol{U}_{ij} > \boldsymbol{E}_{ij}$ then $\boldsymbol{Y}_{ij} = \boldsymbol{U}_{ij} - \boldsymbol{Sur}_{ij}$, else $\boldsymbol{Y}_{ij} = 0$.

If $\boldsymbol{S}^{\boldsymbol{A}}_{ij} = \boldsymbol{S}^{\boldsymbol{B}}_{ij}$ or $\beta^{\boldsymbol{A}}_{ij} = \beta^{\boldsymbol{B}}_{ij}$, then $\boldsymbol{O}_{ij} = \boldsymbol{S}^{\boldsymbol{A}}_{ij}$ or $\boldsymbol{S}^{\boldsymbol{B}}_{ij}$; $else\boldsymbol{O}_{ij} = \boldsymbol{Y}_{ij}$.

If $\boldsymbol{Y}_{ij} = 0$ then $\boldsymbol{E}_{ij} = \exp(-\alpha_T) * \boldsymbol{E}_{ij}$, else $\boldsymbol{E}_{ij} = V_T$.

(5) If all neurons have been fired, go to (6), else go back to step (4).

(6) $\boldsymbol{O}$ is the output of the dual-channel PCNN.

The dual-channel PCNN model inherits essential features from the basic PCNN. For example, the dual-channel model remains the mechanism of synchronous pulse bursts, the exponential attenuation characteristic of the threshold. It is almost coincident with human visual characteristic. It is indispensable for the image processing.

Compared with the basic PCNN, the remarkable characteristic of the dual-channel PCNN is that the number of external channels can easily be changed according to actual requirements, and this is also very useful when several images are fused at the same time.

6.3.2 Image Sharpness Measure

Image sharpness measure is very important for the multi-focus image fusion. Therefore, it is crucial to choose a good focus measure method to estimate image sharpness. In this subsection, some common evaluation methods of image sharpness will be described.

In Refs. [24, 25], the focus measure, the maximum for the best focused image, is defined and it generally decreases as the defocus increases. That is, the focus measure value of the focused image should be maximum, while that of the defocused one should be minimum.

Recently, there are many suggested focus measure methods, including variance, energy of the image gradient (EOG), energy of Laplacian of the image (EOL), and spatial frequency (SF). And they are described mathematically as follows:

Let $f(i,j)$ denote the gray level image with size of $M \times N$.

(1) Variance

$$\text{Variance} = \frac{1}{M \times N} \sum_i \sum_j [f(i,j) - \mu]^2,$$

where
$$\mu = \frac{1}{M \times N} \sum_i \sum_j f(i,j). \tag{6.8}$$

This is the simplest way for the measure of the image fusion.

(2) Energy of image gradient (EOG)

$$\text{EOG} = \sum_i \sum_j (\mu_i^2 + \mu_j^2), \tag{6.9}$$

where, $\mu_i = f(i,j) - f(i+1,j)$; $\mu_j = f(i,j) - f(i,j+1)$.

(3) Energy of Laplacian of the image (EOL)

$$\begin{aligned} EOL = \sum_i \sum_j [&-f(i-1,j-1) - 4f(i-1,j) - f(i-1,j+1) - \\ &4f(i,j-1) + 20f(i,j) - 4f(i,j+1) - f(i+1,j-1) - \\ &4f(i+1,j) - f(i+1,j+1)]^2. \end{aligned} \tag{6.10}$$

The high spatial frequencies associated with the image border sharpness are analyzed and measured by EOL which is implemented through Laplacian operator.

(4) Spatial frequency (SF)

$$SF = \sqrt{\frac{1}{M \times N} \sum_i \sum_j [f(i,j) - f(i+1,j)]^2 + \frac{1}{M \times N} \sum_i \sum_j [f(i,j) - f(i,j+1)]^2}. \tag{6.11}$$

Clearly, SF is a modified version of the energy of the image gradient (EOG).

Among these four measure methods, EOL method has the better performance, so it is used to measure image sharpness in the following subsection. Because evaluation of different focus measure methods is not our topic, more details can be found in Ref. [26].

6.3.3 Principle of Fusion Algorithm

The block diagram of dual-channel PCNN is shown in Fig. 6.11. Firstly, two parallel source images are directly inputted into these two channels. In the interior of this model each neuron can weigh the importance of both stimuli according to the clarity of input images. If both stimuli have obviously different sharpness or clarity, the sharper one should be better and selected. In this way, a sharper fused image will be obtained.

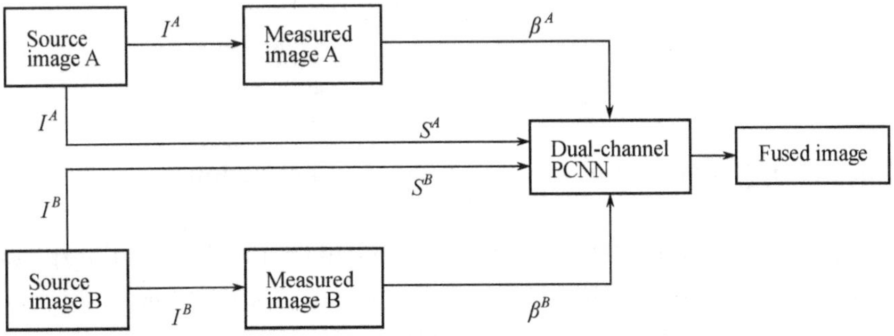

Fig. 6.11. Procedure of multi-image fusion

Therefore, the core of dual channel-PCNN is how to make sure that the weighting coefficients vary depending on the importance of input stimuli.

Here a new method is employed to implement the transformation from the importance of input stimuli to the weighting coefficients [27]. This method is explained in detail in the following paragraphs.

Let $A(i,j), B(i,j)$ denote the source images and $M_A(i,j)$ and $M_B(i,j)$ be the focus-measured images in Fig. 6.11. The difference between $M_A(i,j)$ and $M_B(i,j)$ is defined by $D(i,j) = M_A(i,j) - M_B(i,j)$. Generally speaking, if $D(i,j) > 0$, the pixel value at location (i,j) in image A should be chosen. Otherwise, its counterpart from image B will be chosen. However, in practice it is not sufficient to pick out the better focused image on a pixel-by-pixel basis only by this measure, since the result is vulnerable to wide fluctuations caused by outer environment such as various noises. So, it is necessary to maintain the robustness of the algorithm through more information from neighboring pixels.

In order to make full use of information contained in images, the value in a $(r+1)\times(r+1)$ region centered at $D(i,j)$ is summarized as $\bar{D}(i,j)$.

$$\bar{D}(i,j) = \sum_{m=-r/2}^{r/2}\sum_{n=-r/2}^{r/2} D(i+m, j+n). \tag{6.12}$$

Hence the weighting coefficients are

$$\beta_{ij}^{A} = \frac{1}{1+e^{-\eta\bar{D}(i,j)}} \tag{6.13}$$

and

$$\beta_{ij}^{B} = \frac{1}{1+e^{\eta\bar{D}(i,j)}}, \tag{6.14}$$

where η is a constant.

6.3.4 Implementation of Multi-focus Image Fusion

According to the above statements, the dual-channel PCNN used in the following experiments is a single layer two-dimensional array of laterally linked neurons and all neurons are identical. The number of neurons in the network is equal to that of pixels in the input image. In terms of position there exists a one-to-one correspondence between the image pixels ($I^A(i,j)$ and $I^B(i,j)$) and the neuron ($N(i,j)$). In other words, the external stimuli of $N(i,j)$ are $I^A(i,j)$ and $I^B(i,j)$.

As shown in Fig. 6.11, the implantation of the proposed multi-focus image fusion algorithm is described in the bellows, supposing that the input multi-focus images have been registered.

(1) Calculate the focus measure in Eq. (6.10) for two multi-focus images (I^A, I^B). And denote the measured images by M^A and M^B, respectively.

(2) Compute the weighting coefficients (β^A and β^B) via M^A and M^B.

(3) Input I^A and I^B as two stimuli into the dual-channel PCNN, and then start PCNN.

(4) Fuse the multi-focus images via the PCNN.

(5) Obtain the fused image after finishing the process of the PCNN.

6.3.5 Experimental Results and Analysis

This section consists of three parts: parameter setting, performance evaluation and practical applications.

The setting of parameters is very important to an algorithm. It affects the performance of the image fusion algorithm. But it is very difficult to choose the better parameters, hence, the dual-channel-PCNN's parameters are determined empirically. And its image fusion performance evaluation is carried out in succession by visual effect and objective evaluation criteria. At last, some of its applications are discussed.

Parameter setting

In the dual-channel PCNN, there are few parameters to be set. The weighting coefficients are determined by Eqs. (6.13) and (6.14). The other parameters settings are empirically shown in Table 6.2.

Table 6.2. Parameter setting in the experiment.

parameters	σ	α_T	V_T	r	η
value	–1	0.12	1000	14	0.01

Its convolution core

$$K = \begin{bmatrix} 1, & 0.5, & 1 \\ 0.5, & 0, & 0.5 \\ 1, & 0.5, & 1 \end{bmatrix}$$

and

$$M(\cdot) = W(\cdot) = Y[n-1] \otimes K$$

where ⊗ denotes convolution operation.

For comparison, besides the proposed method, several existing methods: principle component analysis (PCA), FSD pyramid, gradient pyramid (GP), morphological pyramid (MP), and SIDWT with Harr (SIDWT), are also employed. Their parameters are set as:

$$\text{pyramid level} = 4.$$

Selection rules:

$$\text{highpass} = \max,$$
$$\text{lowpass} = \text{average}.$$

Performance evaluation

To evaluate the performance of the proposed fusion method, extensive experiments on multi-focus images and different sensor images have been performed. Here, the experiments are divided into three groups. All images used in the experiment are shown in Fig. 6.12. From Group 1 to Group 3, images become more and more complicated for the purpose of testifying the performance of various algorithms in different environments.

Fig. 6.12. Test images (Groups 1–3). (a) source image 1A; (b) source image 1B; (c) reference image 1R; (d) source image 2A; (e) source image 2B; (f) reference image 2R; (g) source image 3A; (h) source image 3B; (i) reference image 3R

Images in Figs. 6.13 – 6.15 are the experimental results obtained by the proposed methods and several comparison methods, and a reference image is also included in each group of figures. And then the performance of different algorithms is shown with objective standard in Fig. 6.16, respectively. Note that some abbreviations appear in these figures. Their meanings are: CP = contrast pyramid, FSD = FSD pyramid, GP = gradient pyramid, MP = morphological pyramid, SIDWT = SIDWT with Harr.

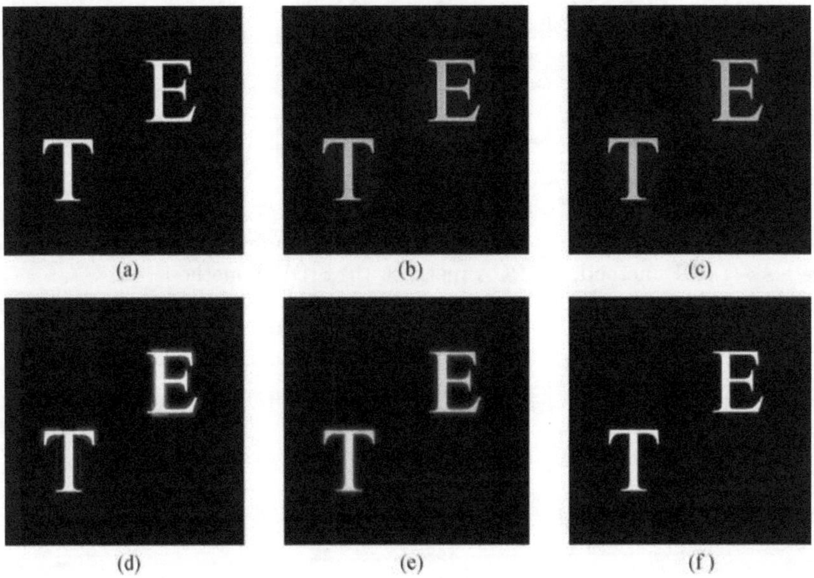

Fig. 6.13. Test results (Group 1). (a) Our method; (d) FSD method; (e) GP method; (f) MP method; (g) PCA method; (h) SIDWT method

For the evaluation of fusion performance, both subjective evaluation and objective evaluation should be taken into account. Subjective evaluation means assessing images just according to visual observation on them and determining which is the best. While objective evaluation means judging images by the value of a predefined function which may be in various forms.

For subjective evaluation, by observing Figs. 6.13 – 6.15 carefully it is clearly shown that the two images fused by FSD and GP methods have lower lightness and contrast than the others. MP method brings forth a good contrast but an unsatisfactory edge, as shown in Figs. 6.12(d), 6.13(d), and 6.14(d). PCA method is very poor in multi-focus image fusion, because its fused image (e.g., Figs. 6.12(f), 6.13(f), and 6.14(f)) is of neither high light-

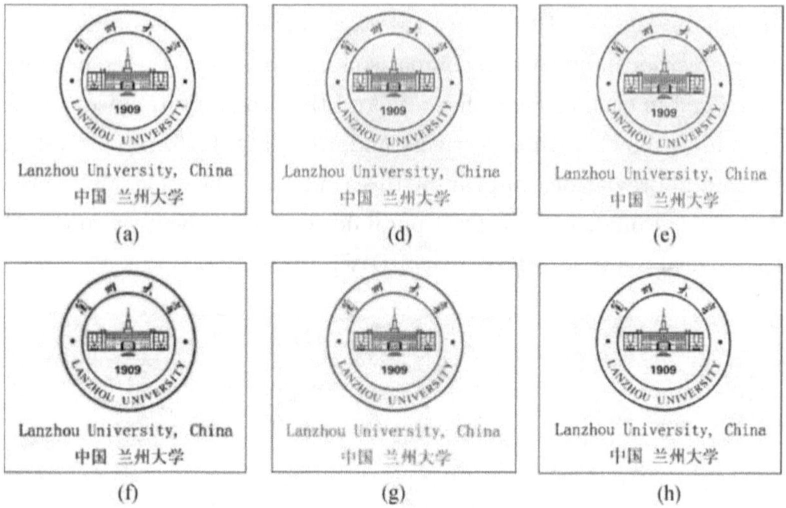

Fig. 6.14. Test results (Group 2): (a) Our method; (d) FSD method; (e) GP method; (f) MP method; (g) PCA method; (h) SIDWT method

Fig. 6.15. Test results (Group 3) (a) Our method; (b) FSD method; (c) GP method; (d) MP method; (e) PCA method; (f) SIDWT method

ness nor fine detail. The rest four methods yield approximate visual effects. For objective evaluation, the root mean squared error (RMSE), defined as Eq. (6.15), is chosen as the evaluation criterion.

$$\mathrm{RMSE} = \sqrt{\frac{1}{M \times N} \sum_{i=1}^{M} \sum_{j=1}^{N} [F(i,j) - R(i,j)]^2}. \tag{6.15}$$

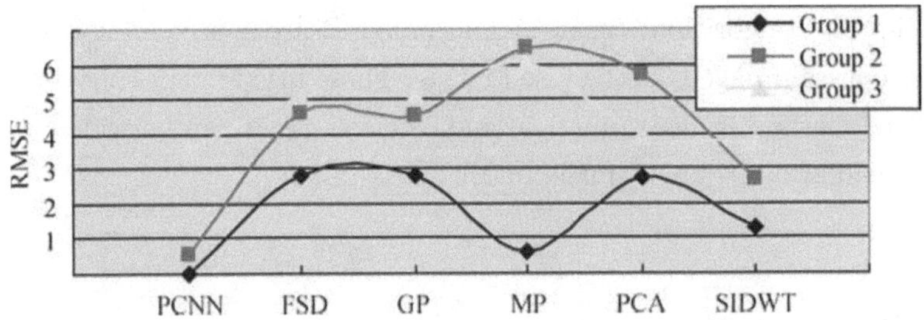

Fig. 6.16. Objective evaluation (PCNN denotes our proposed method)

In Eq. (6.15) R and F are a reference image and a fused image, respectively. Fig. 6.16 records all of RMSEs between the fused images and their reference ones.

In terms of objective evaluation, the proposed method is superior to others, seen from Fig. 6.16. For the RMSE, the smaller the value, the better the performance. In fact, the proposed method produces the smallest RMSE among the six algorithms. As a result, the method compared with the others is better in the multi-focus image fusion. In addition, because experimental images have different complexity, it also shows that the method is flexible for adaptability.

Practical applications

Two groups of microscope images shown in Fig. 6.17 are fused with dual

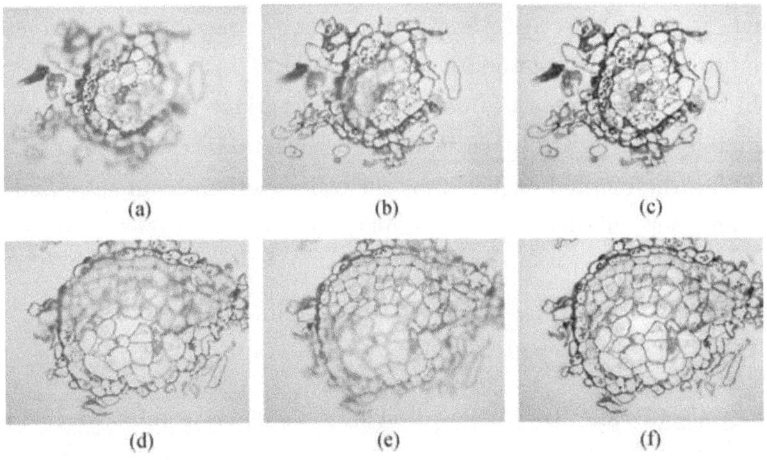

Fig. 6.17. Examples of microscope images: (a) image 1A; (b) image 1B; (c) image 1C; (d) image 2A; (e) image 2B; (f) image 2C

chnnel-PCNN algorithm. Image A and image B are source images with different focuses. Image C is the fused image. These fused images show that the proposed method is more practical and efficient. So, it can be widely applied in the field of multi-focus image fusion.

Summary

This chapter first recalls some preliminaries to image fusion. And then it introduces two methods of image fusion.

Because medical image fusion plays an important role in clinical applications, however, all methods previously proposed do not meet clinical demands completely. In this case the m-PCNN is introduced for the purpose of medical data fusion. Especially, the structure of PCNN is improved in a creative way, and several medical images are used to test the performance of the m-PCNN against other methods and experimental results show that the method is superior to any others.

Then, a multi-focus image fusion algorithm is introduced. Previous methods usually employ more than one PCNN models or a combination of PCNN with other methods such as DWT, while the proposed method just needs only one modified PCNN to implement multi-focus image fusion. Experimental results show that the presented method excels the existing methods in both visual effect and objective evaluation criteria. In practical applications, it has been proven that the method is more efficient.

In order to estimate the performance of various methods, the objective estimate standards are taken in the experiments. The experimental results show that the method outperforms the other methods compared and is efficient and very suitable for medical image fusion.

References

[1] Wang ZB, Ma YD (2008) Medical image fusion using m-PCNN. Information Fusion 9(2): 176 – 185

[2] Wang ZB, Ma YD, Gu J (2010) Multi-focus image fusion based on PCNN. Pattern Recognition 43(6): 2003 – 2016

[3] Wikipedia, the free encyclopedia. http: //en.wikipedia.org/wiki/Image_

fusion. Accessed 12 November 2007

[4] Anderson H (1987) A filter-subtract-decimate hierarchical pyramid signal analyzing and synthesizing technique. U.S. Patent, pp 718 – 104

[5] Burt PJ (1992) A gradient pyramid basis for pattern-selective image fusion. In: Proceedings of SID International Symposium: Society for Information Display, Playa del Rey, 1992, pp 467 – 470

[6] Burt PJ, Adelson EH (1983) The Laplacian pyramid as a compact image code. IEEE Transactions on Communications 31(4): 532 – 540

[7] Li H, Manjunath BS, Mitra SK (1995) Multisensor image fusion using the wavelet transform. Graphical Models and Image Processing 57(3): 235 – 245

[8] Rockinger O (1997) Image sequence fusion using a shift-invariant wavelet transform. In: IEEE International Conference on Image Processing, Santa Barbara, 26 – 29 October 1997

[9] Toet A (1989) A morphological pyramidal image decomposition. Pattern Recognition Letters 9(4): 255 – 261

[10] Toet A (1989) Image fusion by a ratio of low-pass pyramid. Pattern Recognition Letters, 9(4): 245 – 253

[11] Toet A, van Ruyven JJ, Valeton JM (1989) Merging thermal and visual images by a contrast pyramid. Optical Engineering 28: 789 – 792

[12] Kinser JM (1999) Spiral fusion using interchannel autowaves. In: Proceedings of SPIE, Stockholm, 22 – 28 June 1998

[13] Broussard RP, Rogers SK, Oxley ME et al (1999) Physiologically motivated image fusion for object detection using a pulse coupled neural network. IEEE Transactions on Neural Networks 10(3): 554 – 563

[14] Blasch EP (1999) Biological information fusion using a PCNN and belief filtering. In: IJCNN'99: Proceedings of International Joint Conference on Neural Networks, Washington, 10 – 16 July 1999

[15] Xu BC, Chen Z (2004) A multisensor image fusion algorithm based on PCNN. In: WCICA 2004: the 5th World Congress on Intelligent Control and Automation, Hangzhou, 15 – 19 June 2004

[16] Wei L, Zhu XF (2005) A New Image Fusion algorithm based on wavelet packet analysis and PCNN. In: ICMLC '05: the 4th International Conference on Machine Learning and Cybernetics, Guangzhou, 18 – 21 August 2005

[17] Zhang JY, Liang JL (2004) Image fusion based on pulse-coupled neural networks. Computer Simulation 21(4): 102 – 104

[18] Li M, Cai W, Tan Z (2006) A region-based multi-sensor image fusion scheme using pulse-coupled neural network. Pattern Recognition Letters 27(16): 1948 – 1956

[19] Miao Q, Wang B (2005) A novel adaptive multi-focus image fusion algorithm based on PCNN and sharpness. In: Proceedings of SPIE, Orlando, 28 March-1 April 2005

[20] Wei H, Jing ZL (2007) Multi-focus image fusion using pulse coupled neural network. Pattern Recognition Letters 28(9): 1123 – 1132

[21] The Online Resource for Research in Image Fusion. http: //www.imagefusion.org. Accessed 20 Oct 2007

[22] Shen Y, Ma JC, Ma LY (2006) An adaptive pixel-weighted image fusion algorithm based on local priority for CT and MRI images. In: the IEEE Instrumentation and Measurement Technology Conference, Sorrento, 24 – 27 April 2006

[23] AtIas.http: //www.med.harvard.edu/AANLIB/home.html. Accessed 20 Oct 2007

[24] Krotkov E (1988) Focusing. International Journal of Computer Vision 1(3): 223 – 237

[25] Ligthart G, Groen F (1982) A comparison of different autofocus algorithms. In: IEEE the 6th International Conference on Pattern Recognition, Munich, 1982

[26] Wei H, Jing ZL (2007) Evaluation of focus measures in multi-focus image fusion. Pattern Recognition Letters 28(4): 493 – 500

[27] Eltoukhy HA, Kavusi S (2003) A computationally efficient algorithm for multi-focus image reconstruction. In: Proceedings of SPIE Electronic Imaging, San Jose, 20 January 2003

Chapter 7 Feature Extraction

In Ref.[1], Johnson et al. proved that the output pulse images of PCNN could be converted to a rotation, scale, distortion, and intensity invariant time series which is the summation of 1's in the binary pulse images. Refs. [2, 3] introduced some more efficient statistical measures than time series, and used transform to characterize pulse images. This chapter will introduce the application of PCNN in the field of pattern recognition, especially, object recognition with feature extraction based on the PCNN. It is organized below. Section 7.1 briefly reviews some methods of feature extraction based on PCNN, including time series, energy time series, entropy series, energy entropy, average residual and standard deviation. Section 7.2 investigates the anti-noise PCNN feature extraction in the noised image recognition [4]. Section 7.3 describes a feature extraction method combining PCNN with histogram vector barycenter of images [5]. Section 7.4 presents some applications of feature extraction in content-based texture retrieval [3]. Section 7.5 presents its application in the iris recognition system [6], and Section 7.6 is the summary.

7.1 Feature Extraction with PCNN

In 1993, Johnson discovered the feasibility of the PCNN being used to feature extraction. Later, Godin et al. finished similar exploration [1, 7−11]. The output pulse images of the PCNN could be converted to a rotation, scale, distortion, and intensity invariant time series. It has well strongpoint when used for feature extraction in object reorganization, and it will be able to represent a unique feature of original stimulus or input image.

The pulse images are also called binary images because they only have two values of 0 and 1. Obviously, the binary images carry abundance feature information of the original image, but they cannot be used directly as the feature of original image for later classification or identification because of too large amount of the data. Therefore, some transforms for the binary images are needed so that the transformed data can still represent the original image.

7.1.1 Time Series

Johnson constructed such a transform [1,11,12], a kind of sum operation for each output binary image of the PCNN, and then a one-dimensional time series, $G[n]$, is obtained as shown in Eq. (7.1), where $Y[n]$ is the output binary image of the PCNN at the nth iteration.

$$G[n] = \sum_{i,j} Y_{i,j}[n]. \tag{7.1}$$

Johnson named $G[n]$ the time series, which is nearly invariant to translation, rotation, scaling and distortion. The time series exhibits the periodicity. It is very suitable for statistical classification. $G[n]$ realizes the transform from the multi-dimension to the one-dimension and reduced the amount of computation and data storage space greatly. Because of this excellent feature, many derived time series are presented, such as the energy time series, average residual, standard deviation and filters as shown in Eqs. (7.2) – (7.5).

Energy time series

$$e_1 = \sum Y_{i,j}[n]^2. \tag{7.2}$$

Average residual

$$e_2 = \sum |Y_{i,j}[n] - \mu|. \tag{7.3}$$

Standard deviation

$$e_3 = \sqrt{\sum (Y_{i,j}[n] - \mu)^2}. \tag{7.4}$$

Filter

$$f(I_{i,j}) \Rightarrow Y[n], e_4 = g(Y[n]). \tag{7.5}$$

In addition, the CDCT (Carlson Discrete Contour Transform) method is proposed to realize the transformation from two-dimension to one-dimension [13], which obtains good effect but has some deficiency, mainly the poor anti-interference ability.

7.1.2 Entropy Series

Combining time series and information entropy, Refs. [4, 14] presented a new time signal series, the entropy time series [2–4,14]. Entropy is a kind of representation of the image statistical feature, which reflects the amount of information contained in the image. Similarly, the entropy of output binary images is a one-dimension entropy series, $Entropy(Y[n]) = En[n] = H(P)$, as shown in Eq. (7.6), where $H(P)$ is the information entropy of binary image; P_1 is the probability of 1's in a binary image, and P_0 is that of 0's in the binary image.

$$H(P) = -P_1 \log_2(P_1) - P_0 \log_2(P_0). \tag{7.6}$$

Similar to $G(n), En[n]$, the entropy of output binary images is a kind of time series, too, which is variable with iteration number n and unique for an original image. Furthermore, it appears periodicity, and also has the property of being invariant to rotation, translation, scaling, and distortion. And some derived feature extraction methods based on entropy are presented, including energy entropy, logarithm and energy logarithm entropy as shown in Eqs. (7.7)–(7.9).

Energy entropy

$$e_5 = -\sum P^2 \times \log_2 P^2. \tag{7.7}$$

Logarithm

$$e_6 = -\sum \log_2 P. \tag{7.8}$$

Energy logarithm

$$e_7 = -\sum \log_2 P^2. \tag{7.9}$$

7.1.3 Statistic Series

In image signature, Refs. [2, 3] made some other different attempts at the PCNN feature extraction and it is concluded that the average residual and standard deviation based on the statistics characteristic perform higher accuracy than entropy series. Its average residual and standard deviation of each output binary image are calculated with Eqs. (7.3) and (7.4), respectively.

7.1.4 Orthogonal Transform

It is well known that the Karhunen-Loeve Transform (KLT) is one of the classic optimal orthogonal transforms and often said to be the optimal linear transform for the image compression coding technique. After KLT, the most energy of an image will be concentrated on a few coefficients of an $n \times n$ local area in transform domain. Ref. [7] suggested that it is feasible to extract features in the transform domain for binary images of the PCNN. Because of the complexity and consumption of computation of the KLT, it is difficult to apply the KLT directly in real time to feature extraction and to generate the basis of the subspace pattern recognition. Therefore, a set of new orthogonal bases of high-dimensional image space are achieved and one of the important orthogonal bases is retained to form a low-dimensional image space. For example, DFT, DCT, and DWT are this kind of transforms. The information compression capability of sine transforms (DCT or DFT) is closer to that of the KLT. Especially, the DCT is close to the DFT and has a corresponding fast algorithm. Therefore, many transform coding systems are based on DCT, which provides a compromise between the information compression capability and calculation complexity.

A variety of feature extraction methods are briefly reviewed in this section, which represent the edge, texture, shape, and other information. Time series for the output binary images of the PCNN only calculates the number of ‘bright’ pixels in a binary image, and the entropy considers the integrated distribution of both ‘bright’ and ‘dark’ fields in the binary image. Both of them consider the number of pixels in binary images, and the calculation speed of the former is faster than that of the latter. However, both of them reflect the gray distribution information of input image, and also the information of relative location between adjacent pixels, namely the spatial geometry information, which is precisely the key reason why they can be used as the feature information.

The average residual and standard deviation consider the mean and variance of the whole binary image that still reflect geometry information of a binary image.

The orthogonal transform itself will increase the computational complexity, but describing the information of the image itself is entirely feasible.

In addition to these two feature extraction methods described above, there are some other image characteristics used as image features, for example, Ref. [5] took the "barycenter" of the image as the feature for image recognition.

All of the above feature extraction methods can be summarized into two groups, the statistics-based and the orthogonal transform-based, having the properties of translation, rotation, and scale invariance. However, these properties depend on the setting of parameters of models heavily [1].

7.2 Noise Image Recognition

Image recognition is one of important contents in pattern recognition, and until now there have been many kinds of methods proposed to solve this problem. However, there are too many troubles because the original images are usually disturbed with noises, which is a serious challenge in the automatic target recognition (ATR). In general, it is easy to recognize directly simple images, such as digit and simple geometry, but very difficult to recognize complex or nature images polluted with noises. Therefore, the research on dealing with noisy image recognition methods and analysis of noise characteristics is the primary and important issue in pattern recognition. The noisy image recognition is generally based on the following three steps:

(1) analysis of the noise property and removal of the noise;

(2) target segmentation and feature extraction from image;

(3) classification or recognition based on the extracted features.

From the above three steps, it can be seen that the unsuitable choice of preprocessing method tends to lead to a failure of classification or recognition.

In this section, a new method of the image feature extraction based on the PCNN [4] will be introduced. It has the good anti-noise performance for either simple or complex images and can be utilized in the noisy image classification and recognition directly or indirectly.

7.2.1 Feature Extraction Using PCNN

Reference [4] employed the output entropy serials (entropy sequence) of the PCNN as the image feature, and presented a simple method of the target recognition. Meanwhile, it smoothed images with traditional filter, median filter, to avoid the strong noise pollution for the feature extraction of the PCNN. Its main idea is: the entropy sequence of the PCNN is compared with each standard entropy sequence in the database, and the one in the database which is most similar to the input entropy sequence according to the mean square error (MSE) is thought to be the right image, that is, image recognition is achieved. Also, it is very important to set a proper threshold by experience before reorganization, or adding postpositional classifier to entropy sequences for further processing.

In Ref. [4], the MSE was defined as Euclidean distance classifier in recognition, as shown in Eq. (7.10), specially, an original image is sent into the PCNN, and its entropy serial is computed. The MSE between the two entropy sequences is computed and the noisy image is recognized directly according to the threshold value of the MSE, which is set empirically.

$$\text{Euclidean distance} \qquad \text{MSE} = \sum_{0}^{n} \left[G'(n) - G(n)\right]^2, \tag{7.10}$$

where, $G'(n)$ represents the standard entropy sequence of the non-noised image, and $G(n)$ represents the entropy sequence of the noisy image.

7.2.2 Experimental Results and Analysis

In the experiments, the parameters of the PCNN are set empirically in Table 7.1, and L, U, and Y matrices are initially set to zero.

Table 7.1. Parameters of PCNN in the experiments [4].

Parameters	α_L	α_E	α_F	V_F	V_L	V_E	B
Values	1.0	1.0	0.1	0.88	0.29	20	0.1

$$\text{Normally, } W = M = \begin{bmatrix} 0.5, & 1.0, & 0.5 \\ 1.0, & 0.0, & 1.0 \\ 0.5, & 1.0, & 0.5 \end{bmatrix}.$$

Investigation into lots of experiments shows that the entropy sequence is similar to time serials, the entropy sequence of any image is unique and further more, for the same group of noised images, the same frame of image is polluted with different noises, respectively, their entropy sequences are greatly similar because of the image smoothing property of the PCNN.

It will be discussed in the following in detail.

Analysis for Same Noisy Images Group

As shown in Figs. 7.1 and 7.2, taking Lena as one of the test image, the original Lena image is compared with its different noisy ones. The entropy sequences of several differently noised Lena are very similar to the sequence of the original Lena, then a very small value's output from Euclidean distance classifier will be obtained because of the small MSE of entropy sequences between the original Lena and any noisy Lena, shown in Table 7.1.

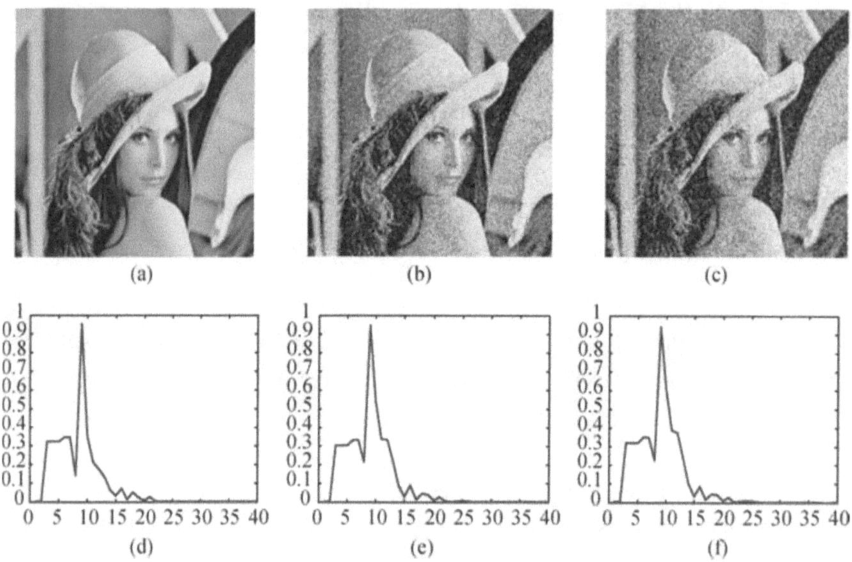

Fig. 7.1. Comparison of entropy sequence of Lena original image and Gaussian noisy images. (a) Lena original image; (b) Gaussian noisy image ($\sigma^2 = 0.01$); (c) Gaussian noisy image ($\sigma^2 = 0.02$); (d), (e) and (f) represent the entropy sequences of (a), (b), and (c), respectively

When the variance of Gaussian noise is less than 0.04 or impulse noise is less than 40%, the MSE will be much small, the object image can be recognized directly; when the variance of Gaussian noise is more than 0.04 or impulse noise is more than 40%, the MSE will be greater, the object image may be recognized wrongly.

The results show that the entropy sequence of Lena is invariant to Gaussian and impulse noises in a wide range.

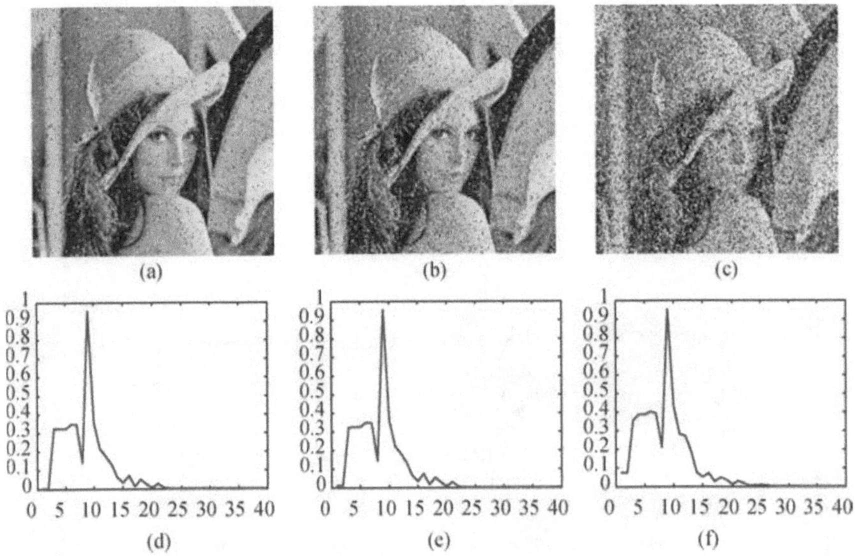

Fig. 7.2. Comparison of entropy sequence of Lena images with impulse noise. (a) 5% impulse noisy image; (b) 10% impulse noisy image; (c) 30% impulse noisy image; (d), (e) and (f) represent the entropy sequences of (a), (b), and (c), respectively

Table 7.2. MSE of entropy sequence between Lena and other noisy Lena.

Noise class	Gaussian noise(σ^2)					
Noise degree	0.0025	0.0064	0.0077	0.0324	0.04	0.09
MSE	0.0184	0.0579	0.0686	0.2300	0.2830	0.5383
Noise class	Impulse noise					
Noise degree	5%	10%	15%	30%	40%	
MSE	0.00004	0.0005	0.0016	0.0553	0.2947	
Noise class	Gaussian noise + Impulse noise					
Noise degree	$\sigma^2 = 0.01$ & 5%		$\sigma^2 = 0.01$ & 10%		$\sigma^2 = 0.01$ & 20%	
MSE	0.1070		0.1253		0.1742	

Analysis of Different Image Groups

As shown in Fig. 7.3, (a), (b), (c), (d), (e), and (f) are different test images (modes), and (g), (h), (i), (j), (k), and (l) represent the entropy sequences of (a), (b), (c), (d), (e), and (f), respectively. Different noisy Lena images are compared with each test image: (a), (b), (c), (d), (e), and (f). And the MSE between the entropy sequence of the noisy Lena and that of each test image is shown in Table 7.3.

Obviously, the MSE of different modes is much bigger, while the MSE

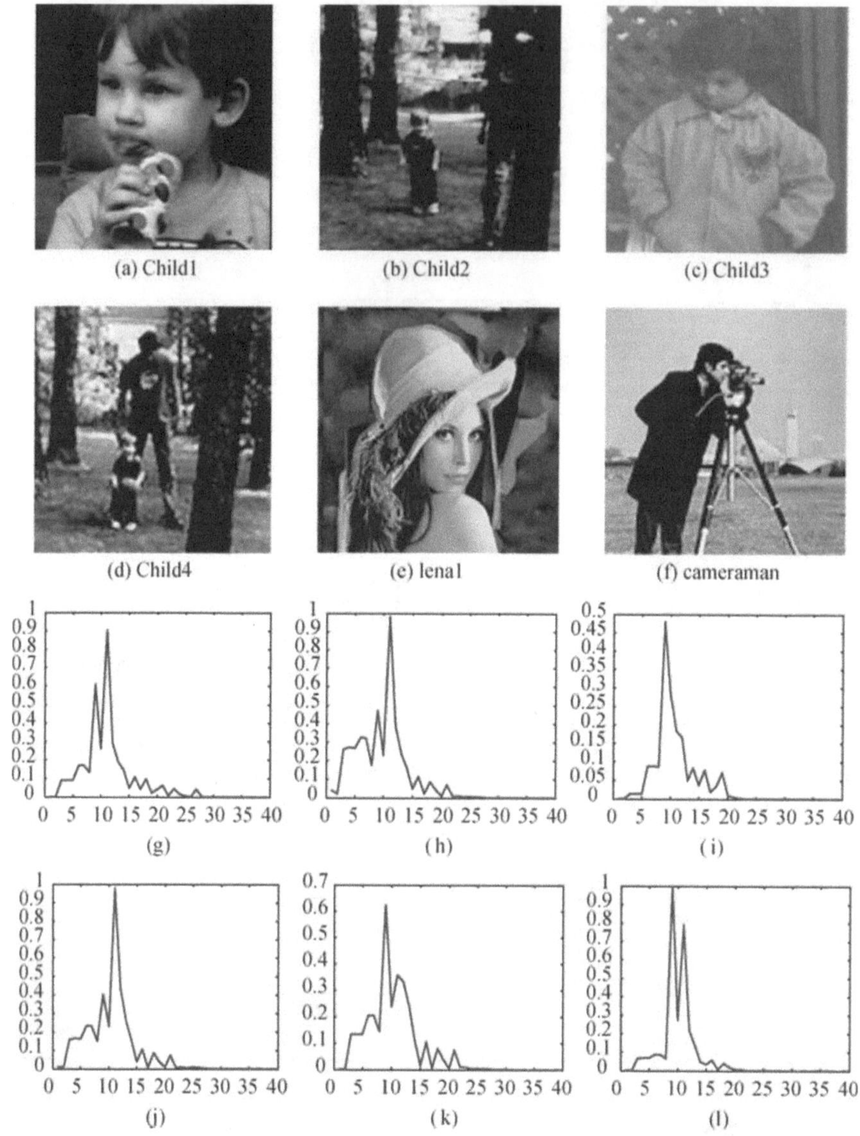

Fig.7.3. Comparison of entropy sequences among other different images. (g), (h), (i), (j), (k), and (l) represent the entropy sequences of (a), (b), (c), (d), (e), and (f), respectively

of the same mode is smaller. With this trait the image can be recognized correctly.

Table 7.3. the MSE of entropy sequences of Lena and other model images.

MSE	Original Lena image	Noised Lena image Gaussian noise (σ^2)		Noised Lena image Impulse noise		
Noise degree	0	0.01	0.04	10%	20%	30%
Lena	0	0.0848	0.2830	0.0005	0.0053	0.0553
Child1	0.8645	0.7317	0.8404	0.8551	0.8623	0.9138
Child2	0.9267	0.7657	0.7445	0.9108	0.8912	0.8440
Child3	0.6656	0.7541	1.1253	0.6727	0.7154	0.8987
Cameraman	0.6827	0.6183	0.8270	0.6799	0.7012	0.8090
Lena1	0.3366	0.3278	0.5581	0.3348	0.3505	0.4321
Child4	1.1080	0.9182	0.9436	1.0935	1.0852	1.0764

Setting of Threshold of Classifier

The setting of threshold for the classifier is very important, but it is related to experiments and image groups, heavily, so it is very difficult to set a suited threshold. Usually, it will be set empirically, here, the threshold is set to 0.3, after investigation into mass experiments.

With this threshold, 100% classification of the object image will be achieved if noisy images (Gaussian noise variance less than 0.04, or impulse noise less than 40%) belong to the image pattern database, otherwise 90% or better classification will be obtained. Similarly, better classification of objects for mixture noised images can be obtained. When images are noised very heavily, it will be necessary to add post-processing, such as special de-noising filters or other pattern recognition networks.

Similar to time serials, the entropy sequence of any image is unique and further more, for the same group of noised images, originating from the same image polluted with different noises, their entropy sequences are greatly similar in a wide range, because of the good performance of the PCNN for the image smoothing. It means that the feature extraction algorithm based on the PCNN is much more flexible to resist noises.

7.3 Image Recognition Using Barycenter of Histogram Vector

According to the introduction of the time matrix in Chapter 2, the time matrix is a mapping from the spatial image information to the time information, giving a genuine storage of the information about the firing time of

each neuron. It not only contains the information about pixel gray value, but also includes spatial position information of image pixels. Ref. [5] made an attempt on a kind of feature extraction methods. It was based on the time matrix and the conception of matter barycenter, and it defined a histogram vector barycenter of image [5] as shown in Eq. (7.12):
Quality of image

$$M_T = \sum_{n=0}^{N} H(n). \tag{7.11}$$

Barycenter of image

$$\overline{n} = \sum_{n=0}^{N} n \times \frac{H(n)}{M_T}, \tag{7.12}$$

where n is the firing moment of the PCNN neuron, N is the maximum iteration number, $H(n)$ is histogram of the time matrix T, M_T is the quality of time matrix and $\overline{n}$ is the histogram vector barycenter of the T.

Investigation into lots of experiments shows [5] that histogram vector barycenter of the time matrix may reflect the image feature truthfully, and it has remarkable ability of anti-geometric distortions (translation, rotation, scaling or distortion) in the application of image recognition.

7.4 Invariant Texture Retrieval

The series of binary pulse images of the PCNN carry abundant information about its original stimulus, which represent unique features of original stimulus, and what's more, the binary pulse images are invariant to translation, rotation, scaling, and distortion. Therefore, the PCNN is particularly suitable for feature extraction. In Section 7.1, some feature extraction representation methods, such as time Series, energy series, average residual, and standard deviation, based on the series of binary pulse images of the PCNN, are introduced briefly. These feature extraction representation methods transformed the two-dimensional images into the one-dimensional vectors and simplified the representation of image features easily. Ref.[3] presented some applications of feature extraction in content-based texture retrieval, especially the application in the invariant texture retrieval on entire 112 Brodatz textured images. In this section, some of them [2, 3, 15, 16] will be discussed in detail.

7.4.1 Texture Feature Extraction Using PCNN

Content-based the Image Retrieval (CBIR) of images, especially those with different orientations, scale changes, and noise affects, is a challenging and important problem in image analysis. Texture features play a very important role in describing the content of images. Importance of the texture feature is due to its presence in many real-world images, for example, clouds, trees, bricks, hair, fabric, etc., all of which have textural characteristics. Feature extraction is a crucial step in any image retrieval system. The requirements for the extracted image features should be significant, compact, and extracted fast so that the image signature is a good representation of the original image. Finding an effective and robust image feature invariant to rotation or/and scale is of paramount importance. Furthermore, besides geometric invariance, it should be antinoise for a real image retrieval system. Refs.[2, 3, 15, 16] suggested some attempts of texture feature extraction with the PCNN in the application of the CBIR. For example, Ref.[3] showed some experiments with time series, energy series, average residual, and standard deviation as texture features in texture image retrieval system. Ref.[2] discussed such texture features' application in the CBIR based on the SCM. Ref.[15] made use of the energy entropy as texture feature, and Ref.[16] proposed a new texture image retrieval method which combined PCNNs with the one-class support vector machines for the geometry invariant texture retrieval.

Figure 7.4 is a diagram for the content-based image retrieval system, the rotated, scaled, or noised image which will be queried is inputted into the content-based image retrieval system, and then its feature is extracted as the signature sequence. Finally, compare its similarity with the signature sequences of image database.

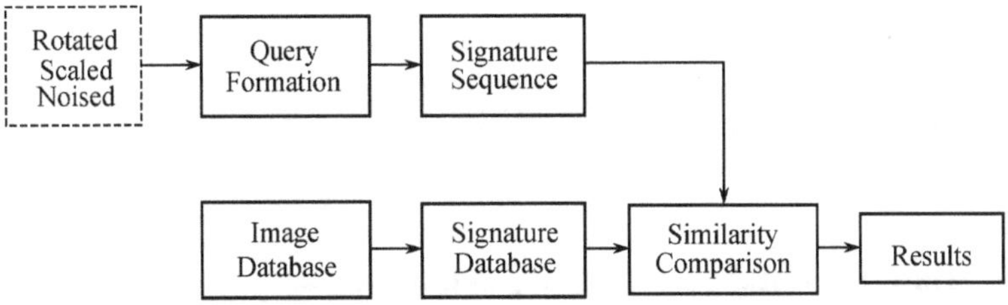

Fig. 7.4. Diagram for the content-based image retrieval system

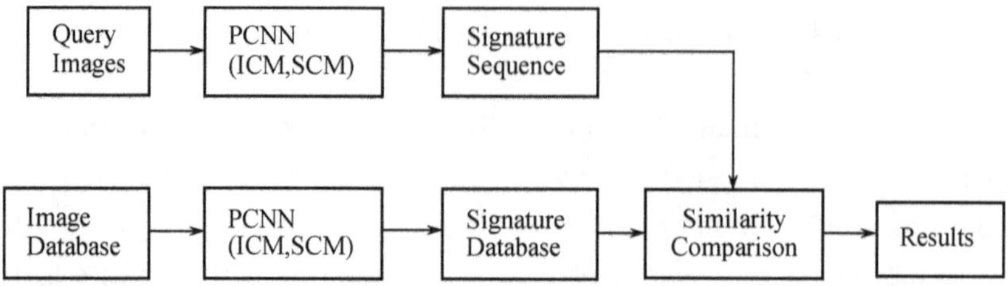

Fig. 7.5. Diagram of the invariant texture retrieval with PCNNs

The diagram of the texture feature extraction with PCNNs is shown in Fig. 7.5. Similar into the flow chart in Fig. 7.4, the rotated, scaled or noised image which will be queried is inputted into the texture image retrieval system based on PCNNs, and then its texture feature (time series, energy series, average residual or standard deviation, etc.) is extracted as the signature sequence. Finally, compare its similarity with the signature sequences of image database.

The similarity is measured with Euclidean distance, as shown in Eq. (7.13),

$$E_d(i) = \left(\sum_{j=1}^{N} (Input(1,j) - Lib_i(1,j))^2 \right)^{\frac{1}{2}}, \tag{7.13}$$

where, $Input(1,j)$ represents the signature sequence of the query image that are the texture feature of the query image, and $Lib_i(1,j)$ represents the signature sequences that are the texture features of image database. The threshold is set as the smallest value of the $E_d(i)$, empirically.

The performance of the invariant texture retrieval system with PCNNs is measured with the retrieval rate, and it is defined as R, shown in Eq. (7.14).

$$RR = N_C = N_C/N_r, \tag{7.14}$$

where N_C is the number of correct retrieval images, and N_T is the total number of images in database.

7.4.2 Experimental Results and Analysis

It is important to notice that no matter what database is used for retrieval, the sizes of images should be standardized to the same size; accordingly, the query image should be resized to the standard size or part of the images should be tailored to the standard size. Here, all query images are processed to a standard size of 128 × 128, especially the rotated image is processed by the method shown in Fig. 7.6.

In experiments, the rotation and scale invariant texture retrieval performance are investigated based on the feature extraction methods described in Section 7.1 and all 112 Brodatz textured images were used as test texture image database. In order to investigate the rotation and scale invariant texture retrieval performance, the query images are geometry changed with joint rotation and scaling by 'bicubic' interpolation and must allow for some distortions from original images. Concretely, in the first stage, crop all 112 Brodatz images to a standard size of 128 × 128 as the standard database and compute image signature for each image in the database, which is performed offline. The second stage is performed online, which requires user to query image retrieval. The query image is typically different from the target image, so the retrieval methods must allow for some distortions. The query image was processed to standard size of 128 × 128 with different orientations (0° to 90° with 30° intervals) and different scales (0.8, 1 and 1.2), and then the similarity comparison was calculated by Euclidean distance.

Fig. 7.6. Rotated image was standardized to the standard size

As shown in Table 7.5, Ref.[15] showed some retrieval rates of these experiments with time series, energy series, average residual, and standard deviation as the texture features in the texture image retrieval system, where r represents rotation angles of an image, and s represents scales of an image.

Table 7.5. Some retrieval rates corresponding to different feature extraction methods.

r,s	$En[n]$	$e5$	$e6$	$e7$	$G[n]$	$e1$	$e2$	$e3$
$r=0, s=0.8$	84.685	84.685	69.369	69.369	84.685	84.685	85.586	89.189
$r=0, s=1.0$	100	100	100	100	100	100	100	100
$r=0, s=1.2$	90.090	84.685	72.973	72.973	84.685	84.685	86.483	90.090
$r=30, s=0.8$	63.964	58.559	30.631	30.631	55.856	55.856	59.459	62.162
$r=30, s=1.0$	74.775	76.577	36.036	36.036	72.973	72.973	74.775	67.568
$r=30, s=1.2$	68.468	66.667	39.640	39.640	63.964	63.964	66.667	72.072
$r=60, s=0.8$	65.766	58.559	30.631	30.631	56.757	56.757	61.261	63.964
$r=60, s=1.0$	74.775	71.171	40.541	40.541	72.973	72.973	72.973	68.468
$r=60, s=1.2$	65.766	63.964	40.541	40.541	64.865	64.865	63.964	63.063

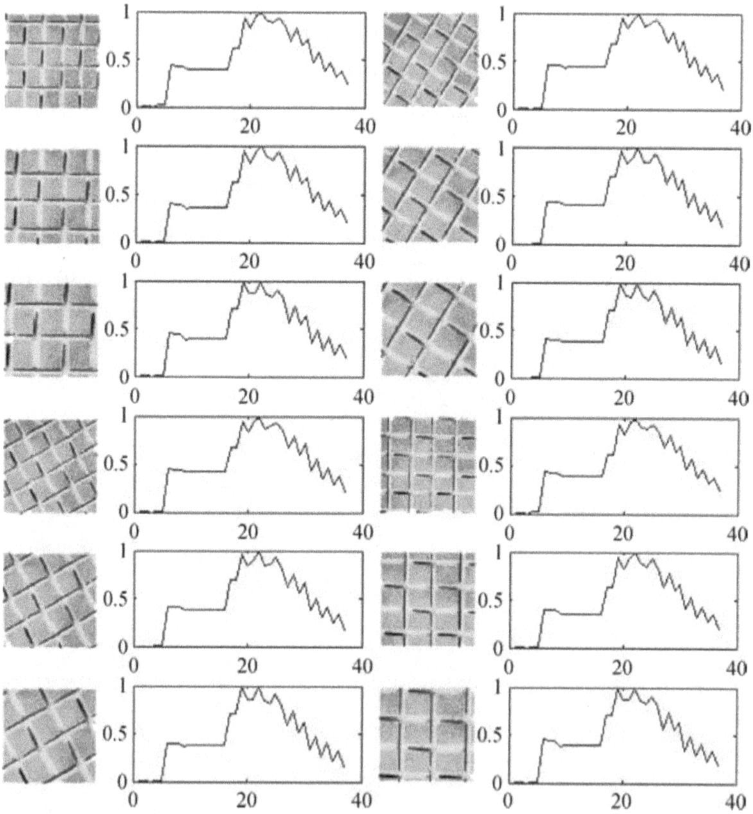

Fig. 7.7. A sample texture (D1) from the Brodatz album with different rotation angles and scales and their corresponding feature images

Reference [3] demonstrated the texture feature similarity of the texture (D1) in Brodatz image database between D1 and its corresponding different rotated, scaled or noised image as shown in Figs. 7.7 and 7.8, respectively. And the corresponding Euclidean distance between the original and the rotated and scaled or noised images (128 × 128) is shown respectively in Tables 7.6 and 7.7. And energy entropy sequence is used as the texture feature of images. Furthermore, the texture feature similarity of 12 textures (D1 – D12) in Brodatz image database is shown in Fig. 7.9, at the same time, the Euclidean distance between D1 and D1 – D12(128 × 128) is shown in Table 7.8.

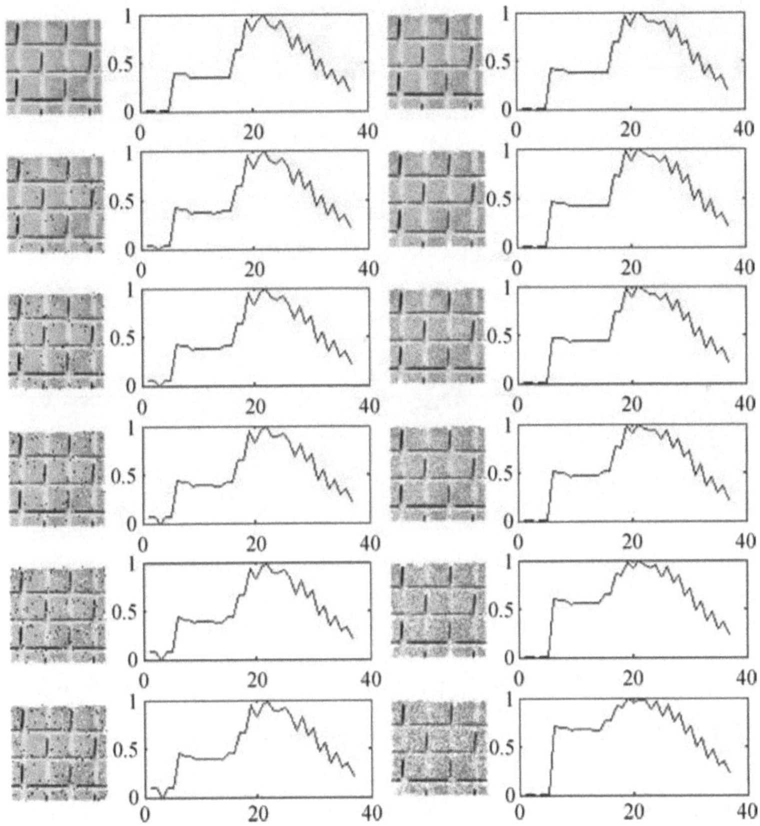

Fig. 7.8. A sample texture (D1) from the Brodatz album in different noises and their corresponding feature images

Obviously, Euclidean distances of different modes are very great. Hence the energy entropy sequence as the texture feature is much more flexible to resist variance and noise.

Two standard sizes of 128×128 and 256×256 were adopted in experiments, and the Brodatz invariance retrieval rates are shown in Table 7.9 for rotation

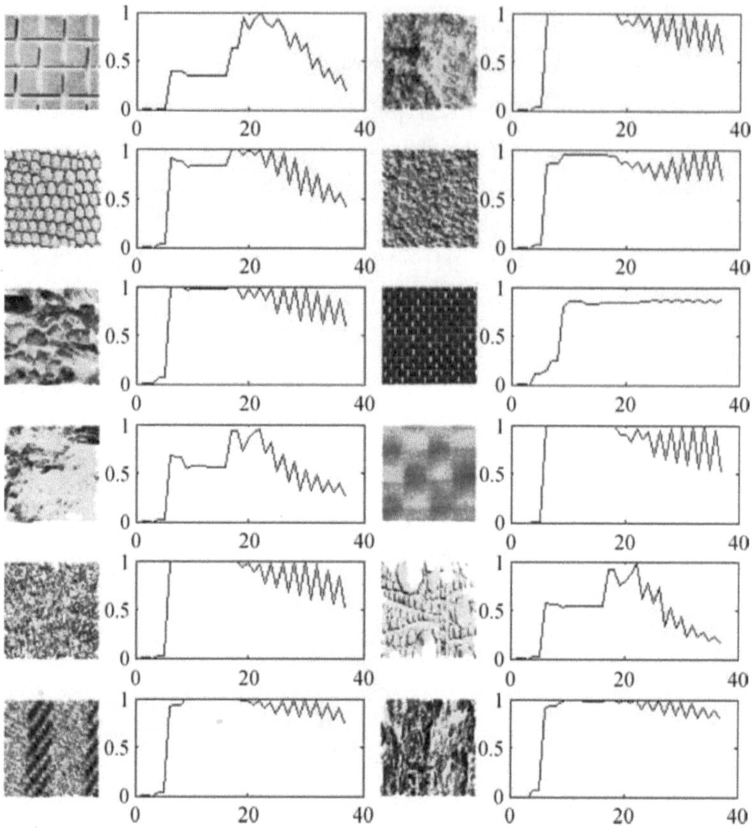

Fig. 7.9. Twelve textures (D1 – D12) in Brodatz and their corresponding feature images

angles and scales. The Brodatz noised retrieval rate is shown in Table 7.10.

Table 7.6. The Euclidean distances between original and the rotated and scaled images (128 × 128).

rotation angles(r), scales(s)	Euclidean distance	rotation angles(r), scales(s)	Euclidean distance
$r = 0$, $s = 0.8$	0.2131	$r = 60$, $s = 0.8$	0.2703
$r = 0$, $s = 1$	0	$r = 60$, $s = 1$	0.2103
$r = 0$, $s = 1.2$	0.2539	$r = 60$, $s = 1.2$	0.2455
$r = 30$, $s = 0.8$	0.2565	$r = 90$, $s = 0.8$	0.2131
$r = 30$, $s = 1$	0.1667	$r = 90$, $s = 1$	0.0103
$r = 30$, $s = 1.2$	0.2634	$r = 90$, $s = 1.2$	0.2515

Table 7.7. The set of Euclidean distance between original and the noisy images (128 × 128).

Noise	Euclidean distance	Noise	Euclidean distance
no noise	0	Gaussian, 0,0.001	0.2650
Salt & Pepper, 2%	0. 0915	Gaussian, 0,0.002	0.3408
Salt & Pepper, 3%	0.1672	Gaussian, 0,0.003	0.4014
Salt & Pepper, 4%	0.2046	Speckle, 1%	0.5113
Salt & Pepper, 5%	0. 2595	Speckle, 2%	0.8465
Salt & Pepper, 6%	0. 2932	Speckle', 3%	1. 1768

Table 7.8. The set of Euclidean distance between D1 and D1−D12 (128 × 128).

Brodatz image	Euclidean distance	Brodatz image	Euclidean distance
D1	0	D7	1.1109
D2	2.4494	D8	2.4682
D3	1.7760	D9	2.4227
D4	2.3328	D10	1.0974
D5	2.4110	D11	2.5458
D6	2.0371	D12	2.5211

Table7.9. The rotation angles($\boldsymbol{r}$), scales($\boldsymbol{s}$), and their corresponding retrieval rates (RR).

r, s	RR (128×128)	RR (256×256)	r, s	RR (128×128)	RR (256×256)
$r = 0, s = 0.8$	84.685%	90.090%	$r = 60, s = 0.8$	58.559%	61.261%
$r = 0, s = 1.0$	100%	100%	$r = 60, s = 1.0$	71.171%	79.279%
$r = 0, s = 1.2$	84.685%	95.495%	$r = 60, s = 1.2$	63.964%	78.378%
$r = 30, s = 0.8$	58.559%	63.063%	$r = 90, s = 0.8$	84.685%	90.090%
$r = 30, s = 1.0$	76.577%	81.081%	$r = 90, s = 1.0$	100%	100%
$r = 30, s = 1.2$	66.667%	76.577%	$r = 90, s = 1.2$	84.685%	95.495%

Table 7.10. The noised image and its corresponding retrieval rates (RR).

Noise	RR (128×128)	RR (256×256)	Noise	RR (128×128)	RR (256×256)
no noise	100 %	100 %	Gaussian, 0,0.001	78.378%	77.477%
Salt & Pepper, 2%	90.991%	96.396%	Gaussian, 0,0.002	58.559%	61.261%
Salt & Pepper, 3%	81.081%	90.090%	Gaussian, 0,0.003	42.342%	46.867%
Salt & Pepper, 4%	72.072%	77.477%	Speckle, 1%	82.883%	83.784%
Salt & Pepper, 5%	62.162%	63.964%	Speckle, 2%	74.775%	75.676%
Salt & Pepper, 6%	50.450%	50.450%	Speckle, 3%	67.568%	65.766%

The larger size of the image, the more accurate retrieval rate, and the higher computational complexity.

The experiments show that the texture feature extraction with the PCNN is quite robust to geometrical changes and noise.

Reference [2] discussed a new neural network model of the SCM which is based on the PCNN. It is used to extract texture features well and obtain high retrieval rate in the application of the CBIR.

Reference [16] presented an improved texture feature extraction method which combined the PCNN with the one-class support vector machines (OCSVM) for geometry invariant texture retrieval. Its main idea is shown in Fig. 7.10. Here the OCSVM is employed to train and predict the feature signature. Firstly, the OCSVM trains the features in the signature database to achieve a training model. Then the OCSVM uses the trained model to predict whether the features of the query image belong to the database, which returns the decision function that takes the value +1 in the database and −1 elsewhere.

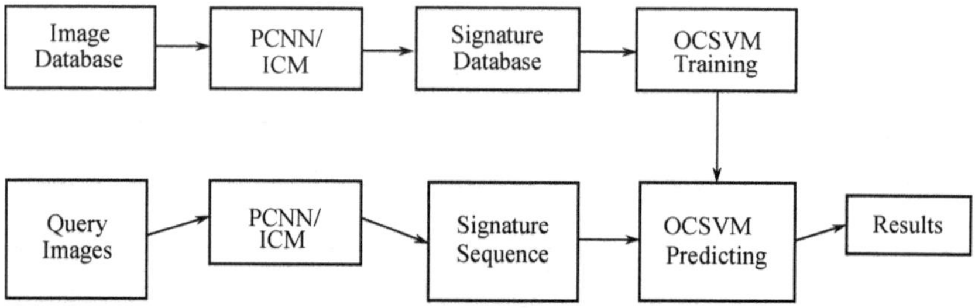

Fig. 7.10. Diagram for invariant texture retrieval

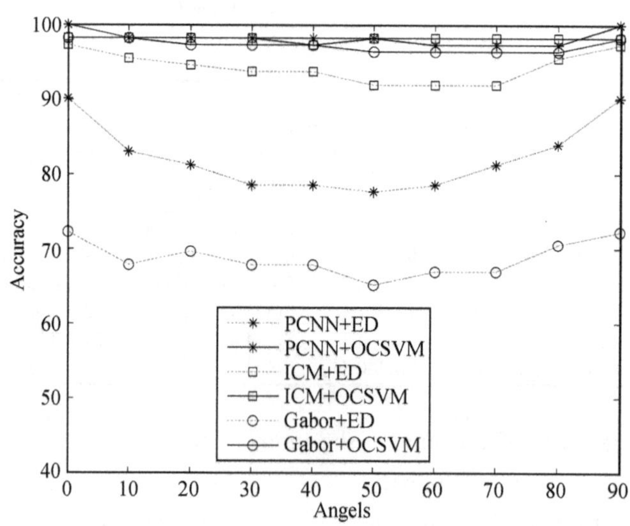

Fig. 7.11. Performance of different retrieval methods, which are subjected to different orientations when all images are scaled up to 1.2

Some experimental results of this invariant texture retrieval system are summarized in Figs. 7.11 and 7.12, where PCNN+ED, ICM+ED, and Gabor+ED are retrieval algorithms from Refs. [3, 15, 17], respectively; PCNN+ OCSVM, ICM+OCSVM, and Gabor+OCSVM are the proposed OCSVM based retrieval algorithms in Ref. [16].

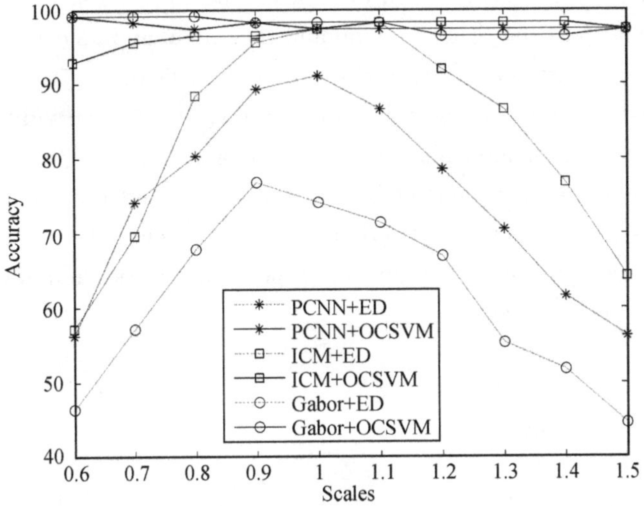

Fig. 7.12. Performance of different retrieval methods used, which are subjected to different scales when all images are rotated 60 degrees

For texture feature extraction with the ICM, PCNN, and Gabor with the Euclidean distance (ED)-based retrieval system, generally the retrieval rate decreases in turn for the following three methods: ICM+ED, PCNN+ED, and Gabor +ED.

In general, the retrieval rate combination with OCSVM is much better than that with ED. Furthermore, for the OCSVM based retrieval, the result is much closed among the PCNN, ICM, or Gabor combined with the OCSVM, but PCNN+OCSVM is steadier than the other two. However, ICM costs less time than PCNN and Gabor for feature extraction, because the PCNN and ICM are illumined from the mammalian vision cortex neuron and closer to genuine biological neuron than the Gabor filter, especially the ICM has lower complexity by reducing the number of equations over the PCNN.

7.5 Iris Recognition System

In recent years, biometrics is a common and reliable way to authenticate the identity of a living person based on physiological or behavioral characteristics. Physiological characteristics are relatively stable physical characteristics, such as fingerprint, iris pattern, and facial feature [18, 19]. The human iris is an annular part between the pupil and the sclera, and its complex pattern contains many distinctive features such as arching ligaments, furrows, ridges, crypts, and a zigzag collarette. Iris structure patterns are very different even if they are twins or multiple births. At the same time the iris is protected from the external environment behind the cornea and the eyelid. Furthermore, it is not subject to deleterious effects of aging. All these advantages let the iris recognition be a promising topic of biometrics and get more and more attention [20 – 26].

7.5.1 Iris Recognition

A typical iris recognition system (shown in Fig. 7.13) usually includes the following steps: iris location, iris normalization, iris image enhancement, feature extraction, and matching.

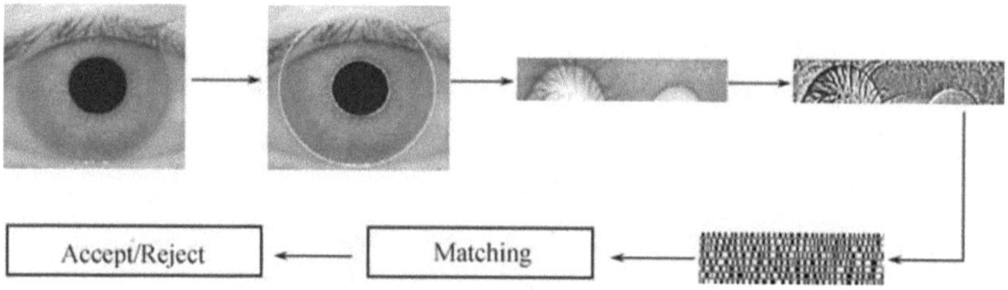

Fig. 7.13. The scheme of an iris recognition system

Iris Location [27]

The iris region boundaries (see Fig. 7.14(a)) can be approximated using two circles, one for the iris/sclera boundary and the other, interior to the first, for the iris/pupil boundary. One location result sample is shown in Fig. 7.14(b). The aim of the iris location is to estimate the center coordinates and radius of the two circles. In Ref. [27], a digital eye image is divided into small rectangular blocks with fixed size, and the block with the smallest average intensity is selected as a reference area. Then image binarization is implemented taking the average intensity of the reference area as a threshold. At last the center coordinates and radius of pupil are estimated by extending the reference area to the pupil's boundary in the binarized iris image. In the iris outer location stage, two local regions beside the pupil area are selected and transformed into polar coordinates from Cartesian reference because these two regions contain some parts of iris outer boundary. In order to detect the fainter outer boundary of the iris quickly, the "summary derivate" which can be got by using Haar wavelet with a constant scale is introduced to locate the outer boundaries of the two local parts. The center coordinates and radius of the iris outer boundary can be estimated by fusing the locating results of the two iris parts and the located pupil information [28]. The location accuracy is about 98.42% for the CASIA vl.0 iris image database [29].

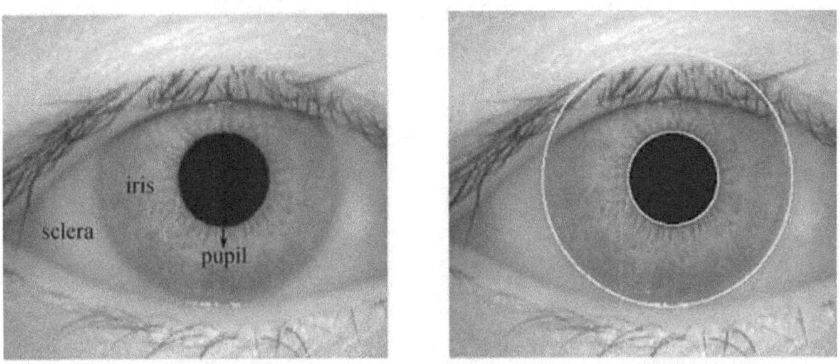

(a) before (b) after

Fig. 7.14. Iris location

Iris Normalization [27]

Commonly, irises captured from different people have different sizes, and even for the same person, the size may change because of the variation of the illumination and other factors. At the same time pupil and iris are non-concentric [26, 30]. In order to compensate the stretching of the iris texture and break the non-concentricity of the iris and the pupil partly, the normalization of the iris image is implemented using homogeneous rubber sheet model proposed by Daugman firstly [30]. This transformation will project the annular iris region to a rectangular region with prefixed size. In Ref.[27], the normalized iris has the radial resolution of 72 and the angular resolution of 360 pixels.

A normalization result sample is shown in Fig. 7.15.

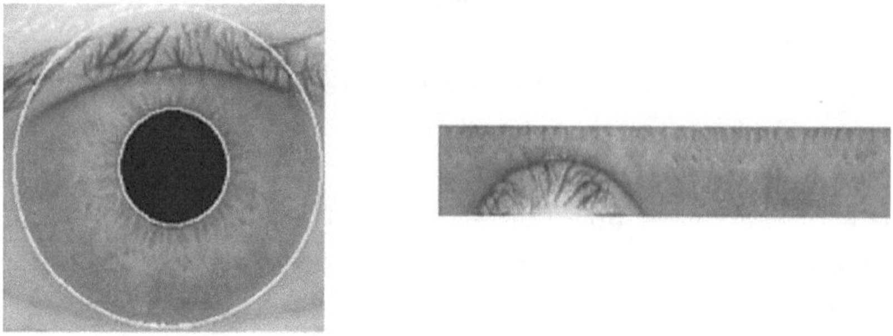

(a) before (b) after

Fig. 7.15. Iris normalization

Image Enhancement [27]

After normalization, the iris image sometimes has low contrast and non-uniform brightness that will affect the following iris feature extraction and matching. In order to obtain a well-distributed iris image, the following processing steps are implemented as shown in Fig. 7.16.

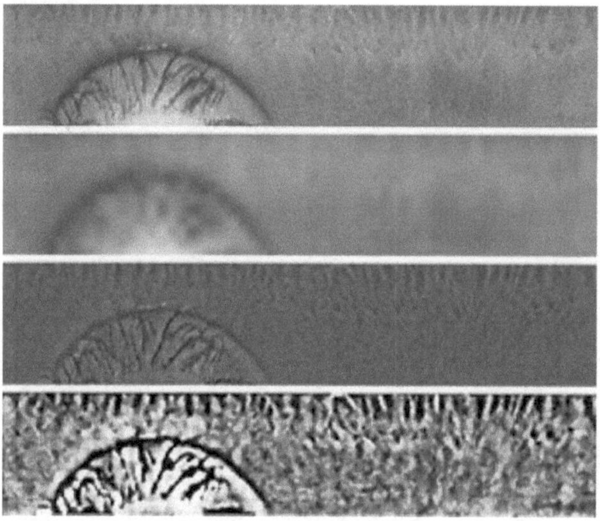

(a)
(b)
(c)
(d)

Fig. 7.16. Iris image enhancement. (a) initial normalized iris image; (b) estimation of background illumination; (c) image with uniform brightness; (d) enhanced iris image

(1) Divide the normalized iris image into 720 sub-regions with a fixed size

of 6×6 and calculate the mean of each sub-region to estimate the background illumination.

(2) Extend the coarse estimation of illumination above to the same size as the normalized iris image using the bicubic interpolation.

(3) Subtract the background illumination from original image to get an iris image with uniform brightness.

(4) Enhance the lighting corrected image by means of histogram equalization.

(5) Use the mean filter to eliminate the noises coming from capture devices and the capturing circumstance.

Feature Extraction

Iris feature extraction is the crucial step for an iris recognition system. Essentially, the process of feature extraction is a conversion from physical image to abstract data that can represent the content of iris texture. However, any existing method of feature extraction cannot efficiently and exactly represent iris's complicated and random texture pattern. Because of its importance, various methods of extracting feature from iris image have been proposed. For example, in Daugman's system an integro-differential operator was used to locate the iris [21]. And 2D Gabor filters and phase coding were used to obtain an iris code with 2048 bits for the iris representation. In order to measure the dissimilarity between two irises, the Hamming Distance is computed between the pair of iris codes. Different from Daugman, Wildes exploited the gradient-based Hough transform for localizing the iris area, and made use of Laplacian pyramid constructed with four different resolution levels to generate iris code [26]. The degree of similarity is evaluated with the normalized correlation between the acquired iris code and database representations. Boles used the knowledge-based edge detector for iris localization, and implemented the system operating the set of 1-D signals composed of normalized iris signatures at a few intermediate resolution levels and obtaining the iris representation of these signals via the zero-crossing of the dyadic wavelet transform [20]. It made use of two dissimilarity functions to compare a new pattern and the reference patterns. Lim exploited 2D Haar wavelet transform to extract high frequency information of iris to form an 87-bit code and implemented the classification using a modified competitive learning neural network [23]. A bank of Gabor filters was used to capture both local and global iris characteristics in Ma's algorithm [24]. And the iris matching is based on the weighted Euclidean distance between the two corresponding iris vectors. Monro used the discrete cosine transform for feature extraction [31]. The differences between the DCT coefficients of adjacent patch vectors are calculated and a binary code is generated from their zero crossings.

7.5.2 Iris Feature Extraction Using PCNN

Generally, an efficient feature extraction algorithm is a significant factor for identifying a person correctly and accurately in an iris recognition system. the PCNN is good at segmenting iris features properly. Therefore, one of iris feature extraction methods with the PCNN [6] will be introduced: An iris's furrows, ridges, crypts, and freckles are defined as the iris texture features, and the iris code will be obtained from binary images of these features, these are output of the PCNN that segments iris features from an iris image.

In experiments [6], the test image database is the CASIA v1.0 iris image database [29]. The normalized image is segmented after the enhancement. And then the output pulse image is chosen as the iris code empirically. Sometimes other rules (e.g. max entropy and min crossing-entropy) are employed to select the best iris code. The parameters of the PCNN are selected carefully through rigorous experimentations and shown in Table 7.11, and its matrices (L, U, and Y) are initially set to zero.

Table 7.11. Parameters of the PCNN in the experiments [6].

Parameters	α_L	α_E	α_F	V_F	V_L	V_E
Value	0.9163	0.7885	0.9163	0.0724	0.0724	10

The size of the linking region is 5×5. M and W are the same weight matrices, as shown in (7.15).

$$M = W = \begin{bmatrix} 0.3536 & 0.5773 & 0.5 & 0.6773 & 0.3536 \\ 0.5773 & 0.7071 & 1 & 0.7071 & 0.5773 \\ 0.5 & 1 & 0 & 1 & 0.5 \\ 0.5773 & 0.7071 & 1 & 0.7071 & 0.5773 \\ 0.3536 & 0.5773 & 0.5 & 0.5773 & 0.3536 \end{bmatrix}. \tag{7.15}$$

As shown in Fig. 7.17, Fig. 7.17(a) is the enhanced iris image, Figs. 7.17

(b) – (i) is the binary image segmented by the PCNN corresponding to the iteration number of the PCNN equaling 4,5,6,7,8,9,10,11, respectively.

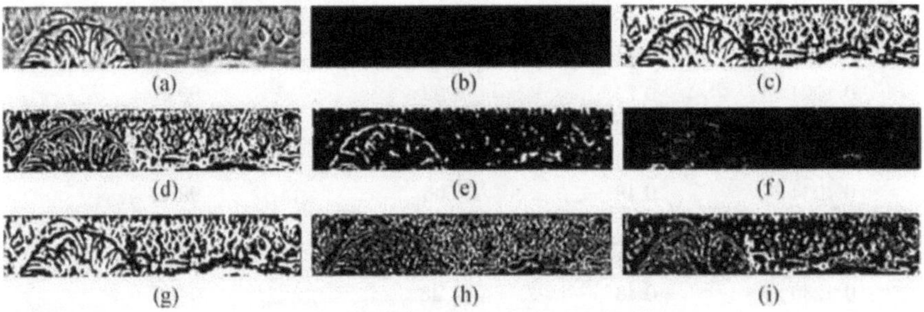

Fig. 7.17. An enhanced iris image and its binary images. (a) An enhanced iris image; (b) – (i) PCNN output in iteration 4 – 11

In Ref. [6], the fifth PCNN output is selected as segmented result. Because the iris region, close to the sclera, contains few texture characteristics and is easy to be occluded by eyelids and eyelashes, so only the topmost 70% section of segmented result is used as iris codes. And then it will be used in the match processing of iris features.

In order to determine whether two iris images come from the same class, the Hamming distance, shown in Eq. (7.16), between input and the iris sample image is used to determine whether the input belongs to the same class in the match processing of iris features [19].

$$HD = \frac{\|(CodeA \otimes CodeB)\|}{18000}, \tag{7.16}$$

where *Code A* is the input iris code template and *Code B*, the iris sample code template, respectively, and the $18000 = 360 \times 50$ is the number of binary image's bits to be compared. The XOR operator $\otimes$ detects the disagreement between *Code A* and *Code B*.

If HD is less than the threshold, then the input belongs to the same class, it will be accepted, otherwise it will be rejected. Here, the threshold of HD is set empirically, too. And its result is measured with error rates [6]: False Acceptance Rate (FAR) and False Rejection Rate (FRR); and the overall accuracy. Obviously, the performance of the proposed method, shown in Table 7.12, depends on the value of threshold heavily [6].

Table 7.12. Different thresholds and corresponding results [6].

Threshold	FAR (%)	FRR (%)	Overall Accuracy (%)
0.3794	2.42	0	97.58
0.3827	2.17	0.001	97.83
0.3962	1.21	0.01	98.78
0.4004	0.72	0.02	99.26
0.4035	0.48	0.03	99.49
0.4052	0.48	0.04	99.48
0.4064	0.48	0.05	99.47
0.4126	0.48	0.10	99.42
0.4177	0.48	0.20	99.32
0.4230	0.48	0. 48	99.04
0.4238	0.24	0.50	99.26

Furthermore, Ref.[6] compares the two iris codes in each of 21 relative orientations, corresponding to the rotation from -10 to 10 degree in origin iris image. And the smallest value of the HD is selected as the threshold because of the head vibration resulting in the iris rotation that would cause the matching failure.

7.5.3 Experimental Results and Analysis

To estimate the performance of the feature extraction method with the PCNN, the CASIA v1.0 iris image database, used in experiments [6], includes 756‘non-idea’images from 108 different eyes and 7 iris images of each eye are taken. Each iris image is in size of 320×280 with 8 bit gray scales. Iris location is finished with the method suggested in Ref. [28]. And 744 iris images are located correctly. Therefore, only these images are used in the late experiments. For the same eye, the first captured three iris images are taken as samples for training, and the other second captured four iris images are taken for testing. The proposed method [6] is compared with other suggested methods [21, 32, 33]. The results of Avila [32], Li Ma [33], and Daugman [21] in Table 7.13 come from Ref. [34]. The results are measured with error rates: False Acceptance Rate (FAR) and False Rejection Rate (FRR); and the overall accuracy. As shown in Table 7.13, the comparison results of different algorithms indicate that the proposed method [6] has better performance.

Table 7.13. Performance comparisons of some popular algorithms for the CASIA v1.0 iris database.

Algorithm	FAR/FRR(%)	Overall Accuracy (%)
Avila [32]	0.03/2.08	97.89
Li Ma [33]	0.02/1.98	98.0
Daugman [21]	0.01/0.09	99.90
Proposed [6]	0.01/1.21	98.78

At the same time, the results of inter-class and intra-class distributions of comparisons are shown in Fig. 7.18, where d' is one measure of the decidability [35], shown in Eq.(7.17), where μ_s, μ_d, σ_s, and σ_d are the mean of the intra-class distribution, the mean of the inter-class distribution, the standard deviation of the intra-class, and inter-class distributions, respectively. The higher the decidability d', the greater the separation of intra-class and inter-class distributions, which means more accurate recognition [35].

$$d' = |\mu_s - \mu_d| / \sqrt{(\sigma_s^2 + \sigma_d^2)/2}. \tag{7.17}$$

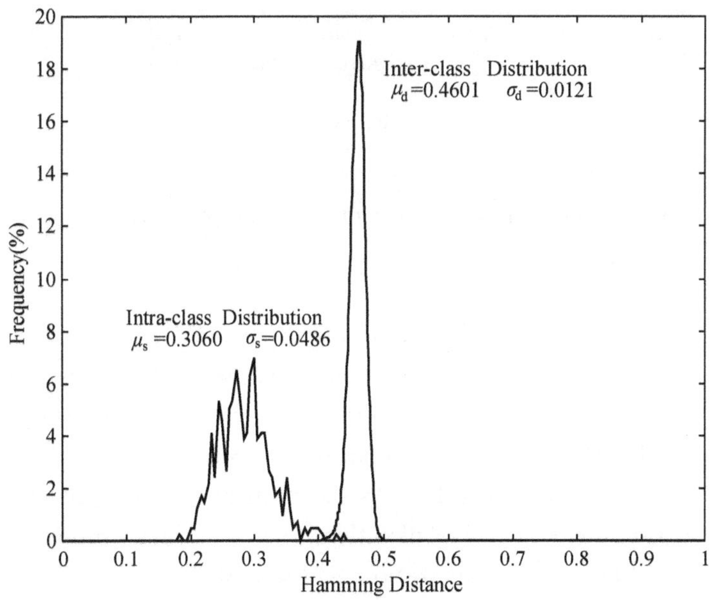

Fig. 7.18. Intra-class and Inter-class comparisons result

And Fig. 7.19 is the Receiver Operating Characteristic (ROC) curve [36] that is a graphical representation of the tradeoff between genuine acceptance and false acceptance rates. Points in this curve denote all possible system operating state in different tradeoffs. It shows the overall performance of a system.

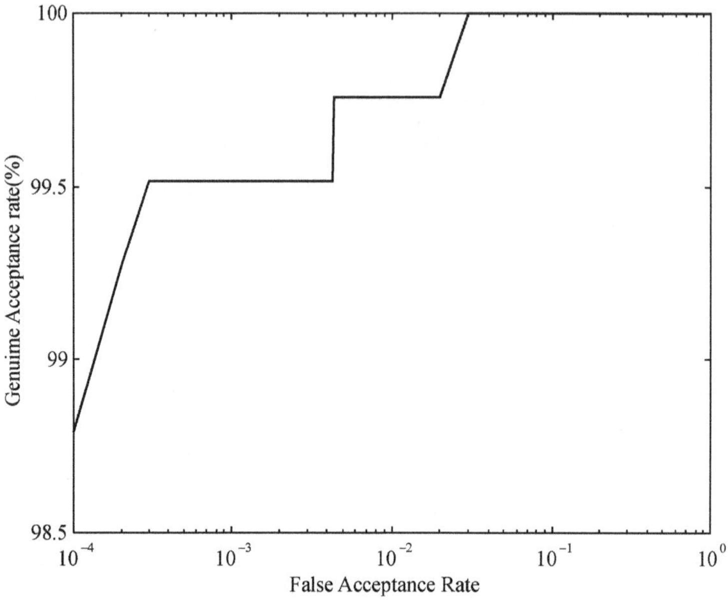

Fig. 7.19. ROC curve

Some false-rejection and false-acceptance examples corresponding to their HD threshold are shown in Figs. 7.20 and 7.21. In this case the separation point is at HD=0.3967.

There are two reasons for false rejection: the first reason is that the iris region is occluded so badly by eyelids and eyelashes that there is not enough useful information for matching, and the other reason is that when the pupil extends too big the movements of textures are not a linear relationship and the normalization model will fail. As shown in Fig. 7.20(c) the textures of right image are smaller in radial direction. There are two solutions suggested: the first is to do a new normalization, and the other is just to filter out the images, having a too big pupil.

Also, there are two reasons for false acceptance: one is that eyelids and eyelashes occlude the iris badly as shown in Fig. 7.21(a), and the other is that some iris images blur because they are out of focus when captured as shown in Fig. 7.21(b). All these iris images should be filtered out in image

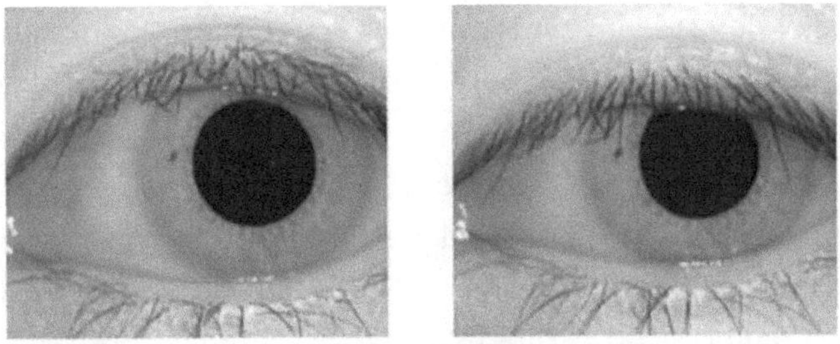

(a) HD = 0.4667

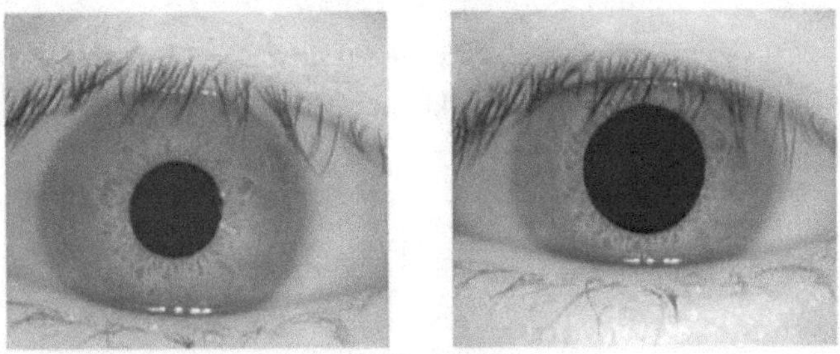

(b) HD = 0.4566

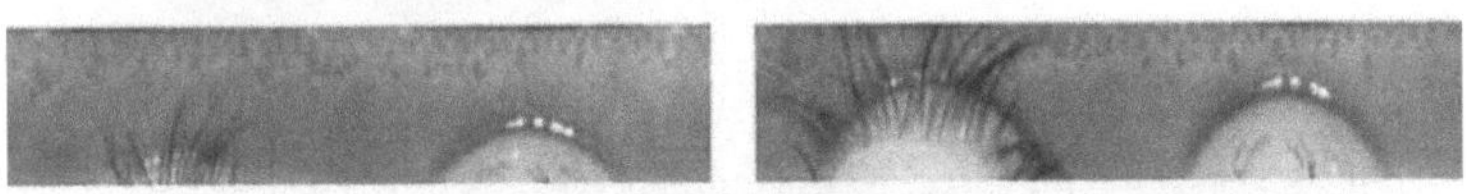

(c) Normalized image of (b)

Fig. 7.20. Some false reject examples

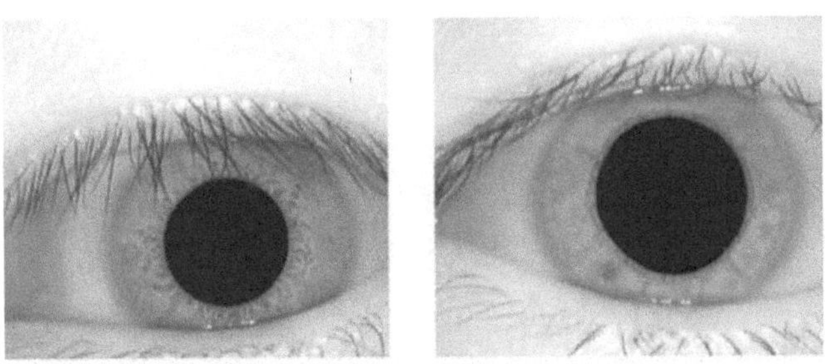

(a) HD = 0.3807

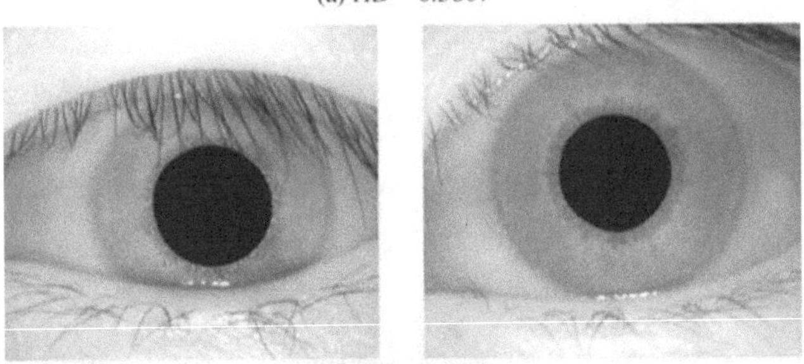

(b) HD = 0.3881

Fig. 7.21. Some false acceptance examples

quality evaluation step before feature extraction and matching in a real iris recognition system. This will ensure the accuracy performance of the real iris recognition system.

Moreover, besides the PCNN, the ICM (intersecting cortical model) could also be used as the segment tool. In a similar manner to what we discussed above, localization, normalization, and enhancement are introduced in the process as preprocess of feature extraction. The process of iris feature extraction developed by using the ICM is shown in Figs. 7.22–7.24. Ref.[27] chooses the 70% part close to pupil of iris region as object to be put into the ICM to extract iris code because the part close sclera of iris region is not

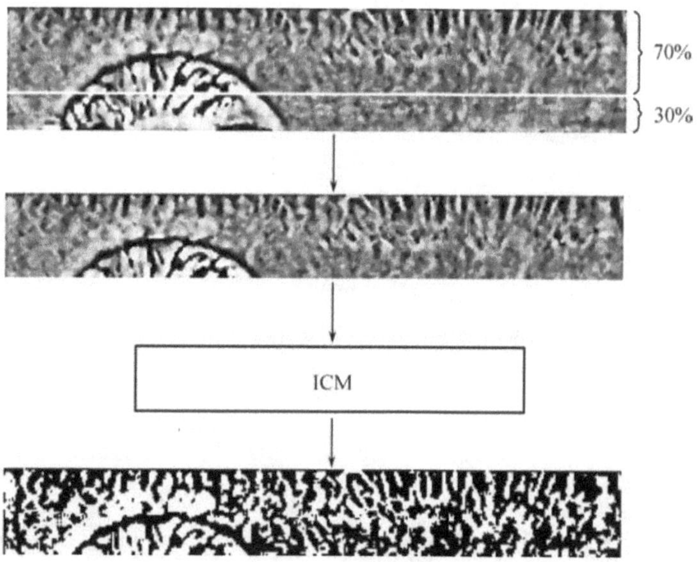

Fig. 7.22. The process of the iris feature extraction developed by using the ICM neural network

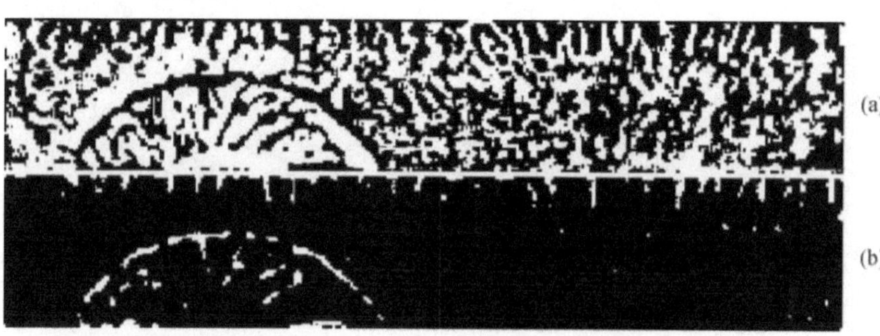

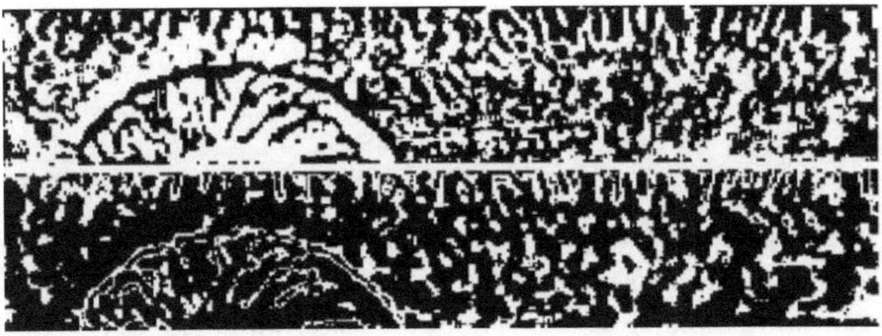

Fig. 7.23. Results of the segment using the ICM neural network after different iteration; (a) – (d) iris feature binary images corresponding to the iteration equaling 4,6,7, and 9, respectively

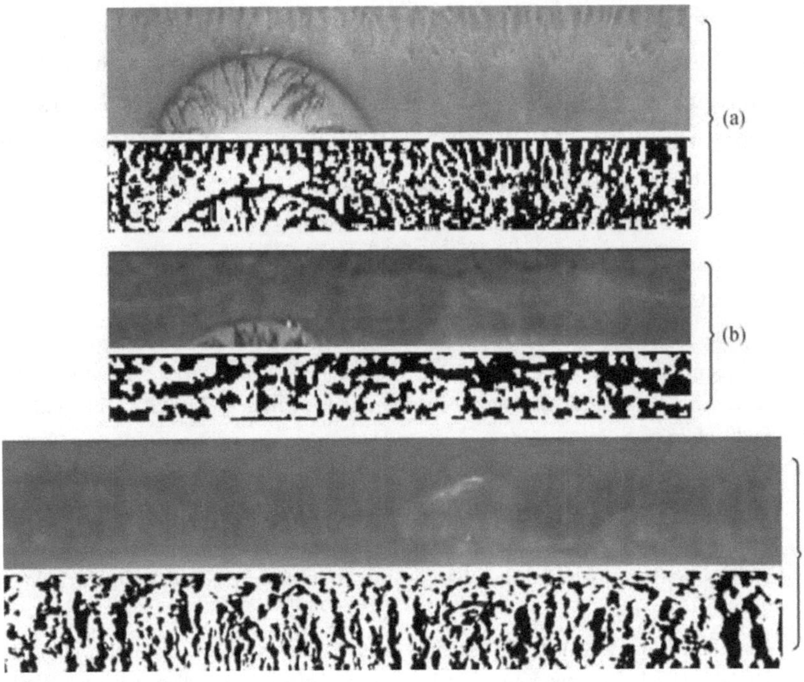

Fig. 7.24. Experiments on different iris image databases. (a) the CASIA v1.0. (b) MMU v1.0; (c) Bath

clear and sheltered usually. The output binary image after fourth iteration of the ICM is chosen as iris code in the experiment. In the ICM, $f = 0.4, g = 0.32$, and $h = 10$. Fig. 7.23 is the results of an iris image after different iteration using the ICM [27]. Fig. 7.24 shows some experiments on different iris image databases, the CASIA v1.0 and MMU v1.0 of Bath, respectively.

Summary

The PCNN generates the series of pulse images, which are binary images and represent different features of the original image. The series of pulse images can then be converted into entropy sequence, which also can be used as image features called the feature of the image. In this chapter, we study feature extraction using entropy sequence, including feature extraction from noisy image, content-based image retrieval, and iris recognition system. On the other side, Section 7.3 presents a kind of feature extraction method which was based on the time matrix and the conception of matter barycenter, it has good ability of anti-geometric distortions (translation, rotation, scaling or distortion) in the application of image recognition. And the results are compared with other methods. Experimental results prove the good performance of the algorithms presented in this chapter.

References

[1] Johnson JL (1994) Pulse-coupled neural nets: translation, rotation, scale, distortion, and intensity signal invariance for images. Applied Optics 33(26): 6239 – 6253

[2] Zhan K, Zhang HJ, Ma YD (2009) New spiking cortical model for invariant texture retrieval. IEEE Transactions on Neural Networks 20(12): 1980 – 1986

[3] Zhang JW, Zhan K, Ma YD (2007) Rotation and scale invariant antinoise PCNN features for content-based image retrieval. Neural Network World 17(2): 121 – 132

[4] Ma YD, Wang ZB, Wu CH (2006) Feature extraction from noisy image using PCNN. IEEE International Conference on Information Acquisition , Weihai, 21 – 23 August 2006

[5] Liu Q, Ma YD, Zhang S et al (2007) Image target recognition using pulse coupled neural networks time matrix. In: Chinese Control Conference, Zhangjiajie, 26 – 31 July 2007

[6] Zhang ZF (2009) Research on algorithms of iris recognition and system implementation. PhD Thesis, University of Lanzhou, Lanzhou, China

[7] Mure?an RC (2003) Pattern recognition using pulse-coupled neural networks and discrete fourier transforms. Neurocomputing 51: 487 – 493

[8] Godin C, Gordon MB, Muller JD (1999) Pattern recognition with spiking neurons-performance enhancement based on a statistical analysis. In: the IEEE International Joint Conference on Neural Networks, Washington, 10–16 July 1999

[9] Karvonen J (2000) A simplified pulse-coupled neural network based sea-ice classifier with graphical Iinteractive training. In: IGARSS 2000: the IEEE International Geosciences and Remote Sensing Symposium, Hilton Hawaiian Village, 24–28 July 2000

[10] Rughooputh HCS, Bootun H, Rughooputh SDDV (2003) Pulse coded neural network for sign recognition for navigation. In: IEEE International Conference on Industrial Technology, Hotel Habakuk, Maribor, 10–12 December 2003

[11] Johnson JL (1993) Waves in pulse-coupled neural networks. In: Proceedings of World Congress on Neural Networks, 1993.

[12] Johnson JL, Ritter D (1993) Observation of periodic waves in a pulse-coupled neural network. Optics Letters 18(15): 1253–1255

[13] Waldemark J, Becanovic V, Lindblad T et al (1997) Hybrid neural networks for automatic target recognition. In: ICSMC 1997: IEEE International Conference on System, Man, and Cybernetics, Orlando, 12–15 October 1997

[14] Ma YD, Dai R, Li L et al (2002) Image segmentation of embryonic plant cell using pulse-coupled neural networks. Chinese Science Bulletin 47(2): 167–172

[15] Ma YD, Li L, Zhan K et al (2008) Pulse-coupled neural networks and digital image processing, 2nd edn. Science Press, Beijing

[16] Ma YD, Liu L, Zhan K, Wu YQ (2010) Pulse-coupled neural networks and one-class support vector machines for geometry invariant texture retrieval. Image and Vision Computing (in press)

[17] Han J, Ma KK (2007) Rotation-invariant and scale-invariant gabor features for texture image retrieval. Image and Vision Computing 25(9): 1474–1481

[18] Jain AK, Bolle RM, Pankanti S (1999) Biometrics - personal identification in a networked society. Kluwer Academic, MA

[19] Daugman J (2001) Statistical richness of visual phase information update on recognizing persons by iris patterns. International Journal of Computer Vision 45(1): 25–38

[20] Boles W, Boashah B (1998) A human identification technique using images of the iris and wavelet transform. IEEE Transactions on Signal Processing 46(4): 1185–1188

[21] Daugman JG (1993) High confidence visual recognition of persons by a test of statistical independence. IEEE Transactions on Pattern Analysis and Machine Intelligence 15(11): 1148–1161

[22] Liam LW, Chekima A., Fan LC et al (2002) Iris recognition using self-organizing neural network. In: Student Conference on Research and Development, Shah Alam, 16–17 July 2002

[23] Lim S, Lee K, Byeon O et al (2001) Efficient iris recognition through improvement of feature vector and Classifier. ETRI Journal 23(2): 61 – 70

[24] Ma L, Wang Y, Tan T (2002) Iris recognition based on multichannel Gabor filtering. In: the 5th Asian Conference on Computer Vision, Melboume, 23 – 25 January 2002

[25] Tisse C, Martin L, Torres L et al (2002) Person identification technique using human iris recognition. In: the 15th International Conference on Vision Interface, Calgary 27 – 29 May 2002

[26] Wildes RP (1997) Iris recognition: an emerging biometric technology. Proceedings of the IEEE, 85(9): 1348 – 1363

[27] Xu GZ, Zhang ZF, Ma YD (2008) A novel method for iris feature extraction based on intersecting cortical model network. Journal of Applied Mathematics and Computing 26(1): 341 – 352

[28] Xu GZ, Zhang ZF, Ma YD (2006) Automatic iris segmentation based on local areas. In: ICPR 2006: the 18th International Conference on Pattern Recognition, Hong Kong, 20 – 24 August 2006

[29] CASIA Iris Image Database (version 1.0). Institute of Automation (IA), Chinese Academy of Sciences (CAS). http: //www.sinobiometrics.com. Accessed 20 Oct 2007

[30] Daugman JG (2004) How iris recognition works. IEEE Transactions on Circuits and System for Video Technology 14(1): 21 – 30

[31] Monro DM., Rakshit S, Zhang D (2007) DCT-based iris recognition. IEEE Transactions on Pattern Analysis and Machine Intelligence 29(4): 586 – 595

[32] Martin-Roche D, Sanchez-Avila C, Sanchez-Reillo R (2001) Iris recognition for biometric identification using dyadic wavelet transform zero-crossing. In: the 35th IEEE International Carnahan Conference on Security Technology, Londres, 16 – 19 October 2001

[33] Ma L, Tan T, Wang Y et al (2003) Personal recognition based on iris texture analysis. IEEE Transactions on Pattern Analysis and Machine Intelligence 25(12): 1519 – 1533

[34] Vatsa M, Singh R., Gupta P (2004) Comparison of iris recognition algorithms. In: the International Conference on Intelligent Sensing and Information Processing, Chennai, 2004

[35] Daugman J (2000) Biometric decision landscape. Technical Report, No. UCAM-CL-TR-482, University of Cambridge Computer Laboratory. http: //www.cl.cam.ac.uk/TechReports/. Accessed January 2000

[36] Park SH, Goo JM, Jo CH (2004) Receiver operating characteristic (ROC) curve: practical review for radiologists. Korean J Radiol 5(1): 11 – 18

Chapter 8 Combinatorial Optimization

Combinatorial optimization is an archaic problem that brings people puzzles until now. This kind of problems are, given the restricted conditions, to consider all risk synthetically, and find the variable that makes the objective function greatest or least. Graph Theory is always used as the mathematical basis for solving this problem. More and more people devote themselves into this area, including many famous genius and amateurs. A classical example is the seven bridges problem [1].

It is said that there is a river named Pregel that divides the town of Konigsberg into four land masses A, B, C, and D as shown in Fig. 8.1. Seven bridges connect the various parts of town, and some curious citizens living in this town play game in such a way as a form of recreation that they tried to take a journey across all seven bridges and returned to the starting land mass without having to cross any bridge more than once. All who tried ended up with failure, including the Swiss mathematician, Leonhard Euler (1707–1783) who is a famous genius of the eighteenthcentury. Euler considered the various parts of town as a point, bridge connecting two parts as a line and he gained a graph. In 1736, Euler successfully explained why such a walk was impossible based on the graph. Besides the starting land mass, one should enter a land mass through one bridge and leave there by another bridge. In this way, from starting land mass to ending land mass if the starting and ending lands masses were the same one, the journey contains two bridges when passing through every land mass. There must be even number of connecting bridges or the walk would begin at one land mass and end at another. But all the land masses of Konigsberg have three bridges connecting with other lands in seven bridges problem. So Euler considered that the walk was impossible.

If drawing a graph of the seven bridges problem where the land masses are represented by points and the bridges are represented by lines, a graph is obtained and shown in Fig. 8.1(b). Then the problem changes into starting from a vertex to traverse the graph, just like using a pencil without lifting the pencil out the graph so that the pencil travels over each line but not more than once. It is not possible to trace the graph without traveling along the same line more than once, just like the pencil does not lift off the graph. Euler translated a realistic problem into a geometrical problem, and the seven bridges problem into estimating of NP question in a connected network. The translation abstracts land mass as point and bridge as line. Euler's method had laid a foundation for topology and combinatorial optimization.

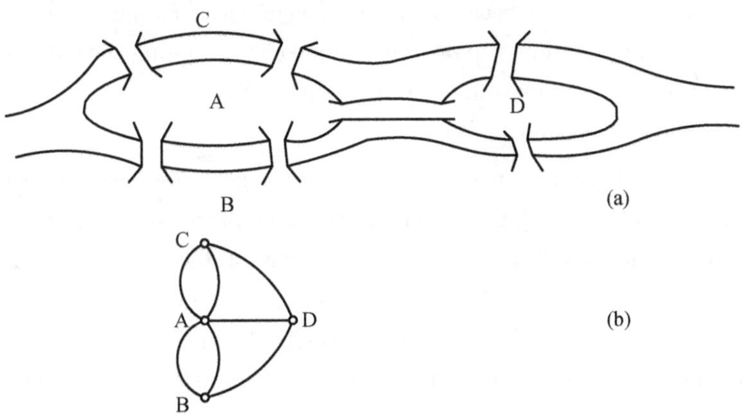

Fig. 8.1. (a) Seven bridges problem, (b) Graph based on seven bridges problem

Define a graph as G to describe the seven bridges problem in Graph Theory

$$G = (V(G), E(G)). \tag{8.1}$$

If using A, B, C, D to represent the vertexes as shown in Fig. 8.1 then

$$V(G) = \{A, B, C, D\}. \tag{8.2}$$

$$E(G) = \{AC, AC, AB, AB, AD, BD, CD\}. \tag{8.3}$$

Given graph G, it contains all the vertexes $V(G)$ and relations $E(G)$ between the vertexes.

In combinatorial optimization, the concept of adjacency matrix is used in general. The logistic structure of graph consists of vertex $\boldsymbol{V}$ and relationship $\boldsymbol{E}$ as shown in Eqs.(8.1) – (8.3). $\boldsymbol{V}$ is the collection of vertexes and $\boldsymbol{E}$ is the collection of the relation (line or arc) between vertexes. A two-demensional matrix is used to store the data of the relation or arc and the matrix is called adjacency matrix.

Some examples of combinatorial optimization are presented as follows:

1) Maximal clique problem

In a graph, a clique is a set of vertexes and every pair of them is connected by an edge on condition that the clique is not the part of any other clique. Maximal clique is the optimization problem of finding the largest clique that contains the most vertexes in a given graph and it is NP-hard. Several real-world and theory problems can be modeled as maximal clique problem. Given graph $G = (V, E)$, finding the maximal clique means finding the subset S that contains the most vertexes under the condition $S \subseteq V$.

2) Traveling salesman problem

Traveling salesman wants to visit each of the given list cities exactly once and returns to the starting city. The goal of this problem is to find the least costly route the traveling salesman takes. This problem is easy to describe but hard to solve. Given the number of cities n, matrix $\boldsymbol{D}$ represents the distance between two cities, and solving the problem means finding the best combination to make the least distance from the starting city to the ending city.

3) The shortest path problem

The shortest path (SP) problem is to find the shortest path between the initial position and the destination in a given network.

4) Integer linear programming

Given an integer matrix $\boldsymbol{A}$ with size $m \times n$, n-dimensional integer vector $\boldsymbol{b}$, and m-dimensional integer vector $\mathbf{c}$, find an m-dimensional integer vector $\boldsymbol{x}$ which satisfies

$$Z = \max \sum cx, \tag{8.4}$$

where constraint condition is $Ax \leqslant b$ and $x \geqslant 0$.

All the combinatorial optimization problems, for example, Eight Queens Problem, Bin Packing Problem, and $0-1$ Knapsack Problem, take up with finding a optimal solution in set F with restricted conditions.

8.1 Modified PCNN Based on Auto-wave

Auto-wave is an essential characteristic of PCNN. Many applications are based on it. In this section, the auto-wave nature of PCNN is represented in detail and a lot of images are shown to display the auto-wave nature. Furthermore, two new physiological inspired models named as auto-wave neural network and tri-state cascading pulse couple neural network, respectively, are proposed for solving the optimal path problems such as the shortest path problem and the traveling salesman problem (TSP).

8.1.1 Auto-wave Nature of PCNN

A full mathematical description of the PCNN is given as Eqs. (1.11 – 1.15) by Ranganath, Kuntimad, and Johnson [2].

As shown in Fig. 1.3, PCNN neuron accepts the feedback input $F_{ij}[n]$ and the linking input $L_{ij}[n]$, and then combines these two components to generate the internal activity of the neuron $U_{ij}[n]$. When $U_{ij}[n]$ is greater than the dynamic threshold $E_{ij}[n]$, PCNN produces sequential pulse sequence $Y_{ij}[n]$.

Obviously, the models produce pulse signals by comparing the internal activity with the dynamic threshold, and the internal status is linked with the inputs and the dynamic threshold changes by its own function.

One of the important distinctions between the PCNN and other artificial neural network is the characteristic of auto-wave as shown in Fig. 8.2. With the principle of the multiplicative modulating and dynamic threshold, in image processing, the pixel with most lightness fires firstly, then along with altering of threshold, inspiring with neighbors due to the function of the inter-connections M and W in the PCNN model, other neighbor pixels with similar characteristic will be inspired and produce autowave. With the iteration of algorithms, the similar neighboring neurons will be fired one by one. This phenomenon is the same as wave produced at the center spreading to surrounding following medium. Under certain condition, the autowave will spread to anyplace where there exist the similar characteristic and neighboring distance. In digital images, autowave can touch the neighbor pixels with similar intensity corresponding to the similar neurons firing synchronously.

A simulation of autowave is exhibited with an irregular object as shown

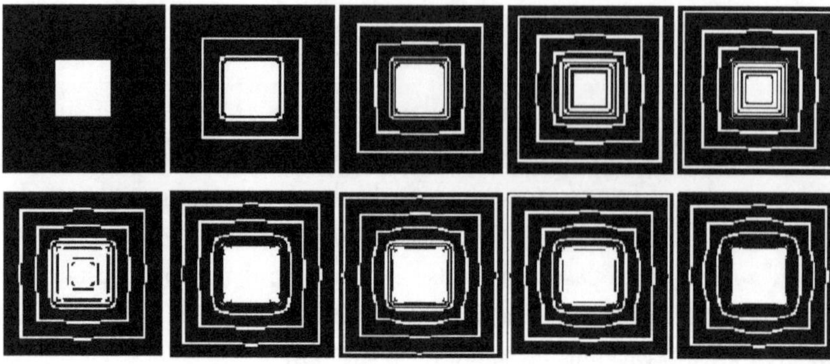

Fig. 8.2. Output of PCNN about an artificial synthetic image to simulate auto-wave (the first one is the original image)

in Fig. 8.3. The autowave will propagate peripherally if one neuron is fired. The propagation is the same as the wave in medium but without reflection and refraction. It means that two waves with different directions cannot go through the other.

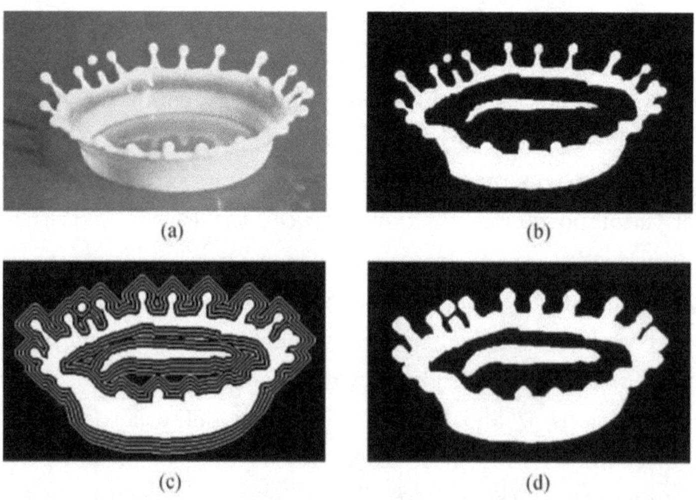

Fig. 8.3. Propagation simulation of auto-wave. (a) Original image; (b) binary image; (c) simulation of auto-wave propagation; (d) all the area that auto-wave propagates throught

Some experiments show that the characteristic of auto-wave (e.g., direction, speed) can be controlled through the change of PCNN parameters.

Because of the propagation of autowave, the neighbors with similar intensity are inspired synchronously with the outer signal and PCNN produces a series of binary images which represent the characteristic of digital image. With the help of the binary image, the relation of pixels will be found.

8.1.2 Auto-wave Neural Network

The PCNN is a system, which has auto-wave spreading and parallel processing behavior. It is based on a neurophysiological model, which evolved from the studies of the cat's eye [4−10]. It is available that the PCNN is used to solve combinatorial optimization problems, such as the shortest path problem. Caulfield and Kinser [11] firstly employed the PCNN to find the shortest path in maze images, but its shortage is to employ too many neurons. Hong and Zhang [12] used adjacency matrix of graphs to represent the shortest path problem, realized full-scale searching, and reduced iterative times by multi-output with linear reduced threshold.

In Ref. [3], a new physiological inspired model Auto-wave Neural Network (AWNN) is proposed. It is especially designed for solving the optimal path problems such as the shortest path problem and the traveling salesman problem (TSP). In AWNN, it represents the problem by adjacency matrix of graphs. And at the same time, it uses parallel processing and auto-wave characters of the PCNN, so it is more efficient to solve the optimal problems.

The AWNN is a physiological inspired spiking neural network model. Each individual neuron is denoted by indices (i, j). It is able to become fired by neighbors when auto-wave goes forward.

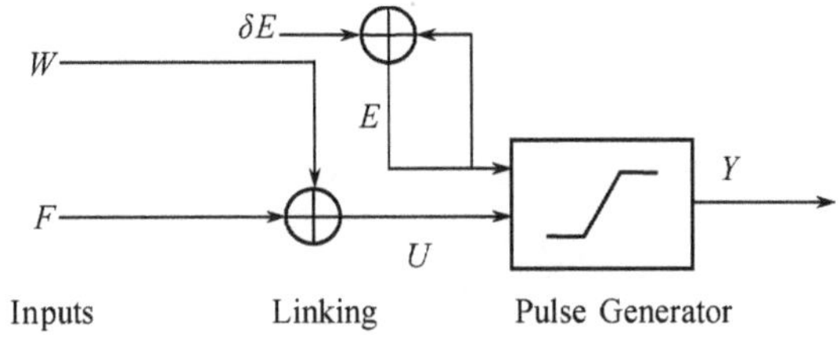

Fig. 8.4. The AWNN neuron model

As shown in Fig. 8.4, each neuron is divided into three components: inputs

$F_i[n]$ and W_{ij}, internal activity $U_{ij}[n]$, and dynamic threshold $E[n]$.

$$F_i[n] = F_h[n] + W_{hi}; \tag{8.5}$$

$$U_{ij}[n] = F_i[n] + W_{ij}; \tag{8.6}$$

$$Y_{ij}[n] = \begin{cases} 1 & E[n] \geqslant U_{ij}[n], \\ 0 & \text{Otherwise}; \end{cases} \tag{8.7}$$

$$E[n] = E[n-1] + \delta E. \tag{8.8}$$

The size of F is the same as the number of nodes of combinatorial optimization problems. F is used to record the accumulative path lengths from the start neuron to the fired one. Eq.(8.5) says the path always reaches node h prior to node i.

W_{ij}, which is described by an adjacency matrix, is the input stimulus. The values in the matrix are the distances between all the nodes.

$U_{ij}[n]$ records the path lengths from the start neuron to the firing neuron. $E[n]$ has only relation to iterative times, and it is increased step by step naturally.

$Y_{ij}[n]$ is the output of neuron (i,j). It plays a role of route-record. If $Y_{ij}[n]$ is 1, it means that the path has already past or just reached neuron (i,j). It is finally used to find the traversal of the route.

In order to decide the iterative termination condition of the AWNN, a sequence M is brought in [3]. In M, the fired nodes are defined as 1, while the unfired nodes are set at 0. As a result, the iterative termination condition of SP is that the end node fires.

With regard to the TSP, the size of M is set at $N+1$, where N is the number of all nodes. The last element in M also represents the start node. Only if the summation of the first N elements in M equals N, the last node will be allowed to fire. The iteration terminates, when the auto-wave propagates to the start node to make the last element in M changes to 1. In other words, if it satisfies Eq. (8.9) and Eq.(8.10), the AWNN stops.

$$\left(\sum_{l=1}^{N} M(l)\right) == N; \tag{8.9}$$

$$M(N+1) == 1. \tag{8.10}$$

Compared with the PCNN, the AWNN dramatically decreases the computational complexity. Since the AWNN uses plus instead of convolutions, it does not have the time-consuming part of the convolutions. the PCNN has five equations and two convolutions, but the AWNN only has four equations and none convolution.

8.1.3 Tristate Cascading Pulse Couple Neural Network [13]

For common PCNN, auto-wave only makes it parallel between offshoot paths of the network. However, to reduce the cost of computation, this parallel processing should be in all directions of auto-wave spreading.

Reference [13] applied the tristate idea of digital circuit design to the PCNN. And the state of neuron is defined as: sub-firing, firing, and inhibition.

Here, the neuron, which is active but not fired, is defined as sub-firing. In this case, its threshold, internal activity, and cost with others are prepared and renovated real-timely, but its internal activity could not exceed its threshold. And the neuron is defined as firing, once its internal activity exceeds its threshold and neuron produces impulse after sub-firing. Contrarily, the neuron is defined as inhibition when the threshold, internal activity, and cost with others are not active, and neuron is idle, also its internal activity does not exceed its threshold, and the neuron cannot generate pulse. On this basis, the process of neuron fire could go through three steps. It could go into firing only if its internal activity exceed its threshold when its state is sub-firing.

Corresponding to tristate gate in digital circuit, sub-firing is the same as high impedance, where the input of tristate gate is real-time variable and every part of circuit is at work, but its output is absent. The neuron will be fired if its internal activity exceeds threshold, then it produces impulse. And the neuron's state changes from sub-firing into firing, corresponding to the high state of digital circuit. Otherwise, the output of tristate gate is zero, corresponding to its inhibition.

For image processing or the shortest path problems, sub-firing is the state in which some neurons joined with it directly fired before and auto-wave propagates as soon as it meets firing condition. In this way, auto-wave realizes parallel processing or pipelining in the direction of propagation. The process of firing is divided into three steps: inhibition, sub-firing, and firing. Network can process neurons in different phases and at the same time network can process different neurons. So, the propagation speed of auto-wave is higher. Fig. 8.5 is the diagram of cascading process of tristate neuron.

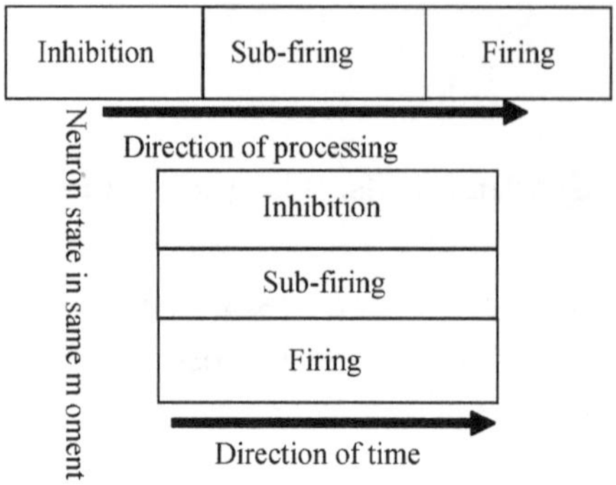

Fig. 8.5. The diagram of cascading process of three-state neuron

To reach higher reliability and improve its accuracy in special moment (for example, many auto-waves in different directions synchronously stimulate the same neuron), accumulative competition is introduced. The accumulation of every path from start node is called intension of auto-wave. Fig. 8.6 is the model of neuron. The summation of auto-wave intension I_j and j's cost W_{ji} is the input of neuron i, where I_j is output of neuron j and W_{ji} is the cost between neuron j and previous neuron. All of inputs compete with each other and the result of competition becomes the threshold of neuron i. So, at t time the threshold of neuron i is

$$\theta_i = Min\{I_i(t - \Delta T) + W_{ji}\}. \tag{8.11}$$

The model of tristate cascading pulse-coupled neural network is shown in Fig. 8.6. Every neuron i has three outputs Y_i, I_i, and M_i

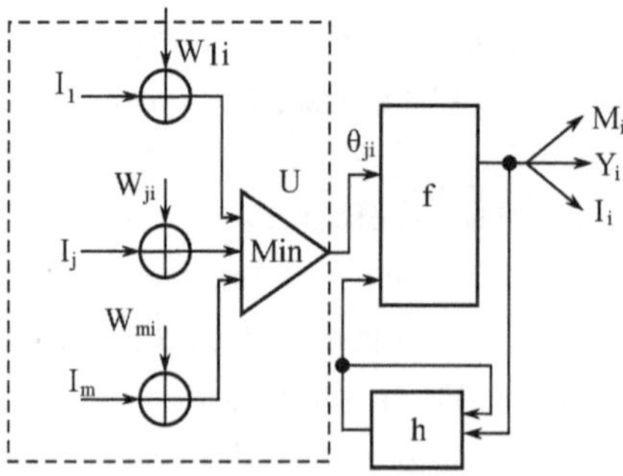

Fig. 8.6. The Model of tristate cascading pulse-coupled neural network

Impulse output is

$$Y_i = step(U_{ji} - \theta_{ji}) = \begin{cases} 1 & \text{if } U_{ji} \geqslant \theta_{ji}, \\ 0 & \text{else.} \end{cases} \tag{8.12}$$

Sign of firing is

$$S_i = \begin{cases} 1 & \text{if neuron i is in firing,} \\ 0 & \text{neuron i is not in firing.} \end{cases} \tag{8.13}$$

Intension of autowave

$$I_i = \begin{cases} 0 & \text{if neuron j is not in firing,} \\ I_j + W_{ji} & \text{if neuron j is in firing.} \end{cases} \tag{8.14}$$

where, $Y_{ji}, U_{ji}, \theta_{ji}$ are the output of neuron i, internal activity and threshold, respectively, W_{ji} is cost or power between neuron j and i.

To deal with the shortest path problem, ordain that internal activity of all neurons has the same power and U changes with time as follows:

$$U = U_0 + X \cdot \Delta T, \tag{8.15}$$

where X is times of iteration, $X = 0, 1, 2, \ldots$.
When j is in firing, threshold θ_{ji} of neuron i is as follows:

$$\theta_{ji} = \begin{cases} V_\theta & \text{if } i \text{ is not in sub-firing or } j \text{ is in firing,} \\ \min\{\min\{\psi_j(t - \Delta T) + W_{ji}\}, \theta_{ji}(t - \Delta T)\}. \end{cases} \tag{8.16}$$

Hereto, the tristate cascading pulse-coupled neural network is designed by Eqs. (8.12) – (8.16).

8.2 The Shortest Path Problem

The shortest path (SP) problem is to find the shortest path between a given source and a destination in a given network or find the shortest path in a graph from one vertex to another. Here, the "shortest" means the total cost correlating with path must be the least or the least number of edges. Same as the well known traveling salesman problem (TSP) and maze problem, shortest path problem is an optimization problem with diverse applications such as vehicle routing in transportation, path layout in robot system, website page searching in internet, data compressing, and traffic routing in communication networks. Here Ref. [13] proposed tristate cascading pulse-coupled neural network (TCPCNN) to solve the shortest path problem, which not only realizes auto-wave in PCNNs, but also acquires its own longitudinal processing.

8.2.1 Algorithm for Shortest Path Problems Based on TCPCNN

In this algorithm, inflexion in path only corresponds with neuron. The coupling between neurons is represented by connective power. The application of discrete form of the TCPCNN in the shortest path problem is described as follows (the symbols used in this algorithm are shown in Table 8.1).

Table 8.1. Symbols used in TCPCNN algorithm

Symbol	Description	Symbol	Description
start	initiatory firing node	*ends*	concluding firing node
i	current node	j	previous firing node before i
x	current iterative number	w	table of connective power
t	current time	δt	time difference between iteration

1) Initialize network

$$U = U_0;\ \theta_{ji} = V_\theta;\ Y_{ji} = 0; I_j = 0;\ \text{Set } W_{ji}, \forall j, i \in V.$$

2) Activate network

To the start node, set $\theta = 0$, $Y_{start,start} = 1, I_{start} = 0$; make neuron x into sub-firing where $W_{start,x} \neq 0$, and calculate $W_{start,x}$, U, $\theta_{start,x}$.

3) Renovate network

autowave emanates from *start* in all directions. After every iteration, look for the sub-firing node and judge whether it meets the firing condition. If neuron x satisfies the condition, it will fire at once and change its output: Y, I, M. At the same time, find out the node k whose value is not zero in x row of w. Then judge M_k, if $M_k = 0$, this node runs into sub-firing; else $M_k = 1$, update $U(t) = U(t - \Delta T) + \Delta T$, repeat (3).

4) Finish iteration

when destination, *ends*, has fired, iteration is finished, and the shortest path is sought out.

5) Trace path

look for the entire nodes in the shortest path by output table Y, record the whole path.

The algorithm can obtain the shortest path from single node to single node or to multi-node, and can seek out full-scale optimization solution. On the other hand, the shortest path from single node to multi-node can be found by propagating of auto-wave only once.

8.2.2 Experimental Results and Analysis

The algorithm was implemented in Matlab platform with PC (AMD Athlon 2200+ (1.75 GHz), 256 MB memory). The illustration of algorithm with an undirected weighted graph is shown in Fig. 8.7. It contains 12 vertexes and 26 edges. The connective power between two vertexes is marked beside edge.

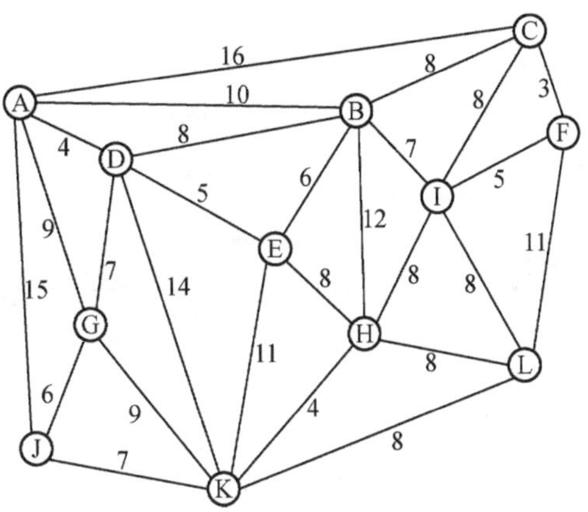

Fig. 8.7. Undirected weighted graph

In this experiment $V_\theta = 200$, $\Delta T = 1$. In other words, the internal activity increases by one in every iteration. At any moment, internal activities of all neurons are the same, but their thresholds are different. Different start nodes have different U_0. In this way iterative numbers are reduced.

Auto-wave emanated from any node can run through the whole network as long as befitting V_θ, and the searching process of the shortest path is full-scale. The experimental results are based on Fig. 8.8. Table 8.2 is the searching results from single node to single node. Table 8.3 is the result from single node to multi-node (here $U_0 = 3$). The most obvious advantage of this method is less time-consuming in the average cost of every iteration. Iteration is parallel in time, and at the same time there are several iterations in different steps. The total cost time is reduced, the average cost is reduced greatly, and the speed of algorithm is increased, too.

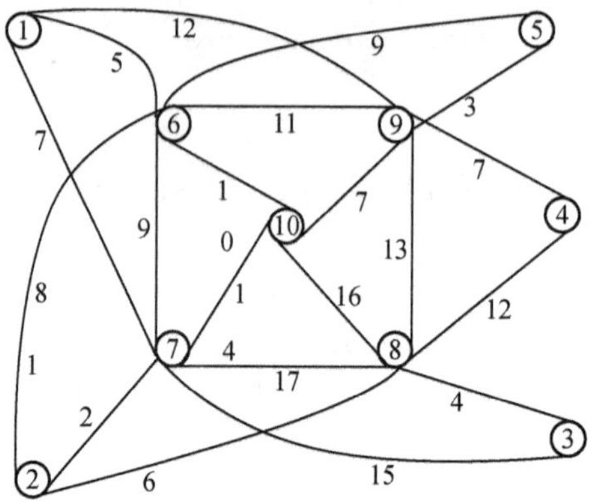

Fig. 8.8. Undirected weighted graph used in Ref [11]

Table.8.2. Searching result from single node to single node.

Start	End	Shortest Path	Iterative Number	Cast	Full-Scale Searching
A	L	A→D→E→H→L	22	25	Yes
L	A	L→I→B→A	22	25	Yes
C	J	D→I→H→K→J	25	27	Yes
J	C	J→K→H→I→D	25	27	Yes

Table.8.3. Searching result from single node to multi-node

Start	End	Shortest Path	Iterative Number	Cast	Full-Scale Searching
A	B	A→B	7	10	Yes
A	C	A→C	13	16	Yes
A	D	A→D	1	4	Yes
A	E	A→D→E	6	9	Yes
A	F	A→C→F	16	19	Yes
A	G	A→G	6	9	Yes
A	H	A→D→E→H	14	17	Yes
A	I	A→B→I	14	17	Yes
A	J	A→J	12	15	Yes
A	K	A→D→K	15	18	Yes
A	L	A→D→E→H→L	22	25	Yes

This algorithm is applied to Fig. 8.8 which came from Ref. [12]. Table 8.4

is experimental results about the algorithm in this section. Here, the initial internal activity U_0 is the intensity of auto-wave when the node (which is the closed one to *start*) is in firing. Not only iterative number is reduced, but also time cost of iteration is reduced. Table 8.4 is the compared results of iterative numbers barely.

Table.8.4. Compared results of TCPCNN for the graph in Fig. 8.8 (SF_{Pro} denotes the proposed algorithm while $SF_{[12]}$ denotes algorithm in Ref. [12]).

start	Shortest path	Iterative number		Full-scale searching
		SF_{Pro}	$SF_{[12]}$	
1	1→7→2 ; 1→7→2→8→3 ; 1→9→4 ; 1→6→5 ; 1→6→10	15	23	Yes
2	2→6→5 ; 2→7→1 ; 2→7→10 ; 2→8→3 ; 2→8→4 ; 2→8→9	18	21	Yes
3	3→8→2→6;3→8→2→7→1;3→8→4; 3→8→9→5;3→8→10	17	23	Yes
4	4→8→2 ; 4→8→3 ; 4→8→2→7 ; 4→9→5 ; 4→9→6 ; 4→9→10	14	29	Yes
5	5→6→1 ; 5→6→2 ; 5→6→7 ; 5→9→4 ; 5→9→8→3 ; 5→9→10	18	23	Yes
6	6→2→8→3 ; 6→9→4	10	21	Yes
7	7→6→5 ; 7→2→8→3 ; 7→2→8→4	18	25	Yes
8	8→2→6 ; 8→2→7→1 ; 8→9→5 ; 8→10	13	28	Yes
9	9→1→7 ; 9→6→2 ; 9→8→3	17	21	Yes
10	10→6→1 ; 10→7→2 ; 10→8→3 ; 10→9→4 ; 10→9→5	14	22	Yes

To illuminate the independence on parameters, six experiments were conducted. The start node is A, and end node is L. Experimental results with different parameters can be seen in Table 8.5. The experiment result shows that the proposed algorithm can find out the shortest path, increase searching speed and gain better result as long as there are suitable parameters $\Delta T, V_\theta, U_0$. In addition, parameters can be chosen in a wider range.

Table.8.5. Result and parameters.

No	parameters				
	ΔT	V	U_0	Iterative number	correct
1 (A→L)	1	200	3.5	22	Yes
2 (A→L)	2	200	3.5	23	Yes
3 (A→L)	1	200	3.5	22	Yes
4 (A→L)	1	200	3.0	22	yes
5 (A→L)	1	200	2.5	24	Yes
6 (A→L)	1	200	0.5	21	Yes

The TCPCNN realizes parallel processing in both the spreading direction and the transverse direction. It increases searching speed and ensures accuracy via accumulative competition. It has little dependence on initial conditions and parameters.

The algorithm can also be used in continuous-time path problem. When delta is small enough, the discrete problem is translated into continuous-time network.

8.3 Traveling Salesman Problem

Traveling salesman Problem (TSP) is a representative hard to solve problem in combinatorial optimization. In this section, an algorithm based on AWNN for optimal problems is proposed and some experimental results show its performance.

8.3.1 Algorithm for Optimal Problems Based on AWNN

Algorithms for optimal path problems especially for traveling salesman problem using AWNN will be presented in this section.

In Eqs. (8.5) – (8.8), Y is defined as the output of the AWNN, and U is the activity status of the AWNN. $Y_{ij}[0]$ and $U_{ij}[0]$ are initially set at zero. If a node is fired for the first time, the corresponding rows of values in W and U are the same. In the following iterations, $U_{ij}[n]$ would be changed when some previous nodes let current nodes fire. At this time, $U_{ij}[n]$ of firing node will increase by $F_i[n]$. So $U_{ij}[n]$ represents the history paths lengths of the firing node.

In the experiment, initially set $E[0]$ at a value that is lower than any value in W, and δE is lower than any difference values in W. If all values in W are integers, δE can be set at 1. Set $F_i[0] = 0$ and $M_i[0] = 0$.

If the *ith* node has fired, F_i records the path length of this node. So every element value in F changes only once.

Accompanied by propagation of autowave, the internal status $U_{ij}[n]$ is changed, and $E[n]$ is increased by δE step by step naturally. When the value of $E[n]$ reaches the minimum values in $U_{ij}[n]$, these nodes would be fired and their values in $U_{ij}[n]$ would be changed.

Figure 8.9 is a simple undirected weighted graph. Let city A fire at first. For getting the shortest path from A to D, its corresponding adjacency matrix W is Eq.(8.17).

$$W = \begin{bmatrix} 0 & 2 & 3 & 7 & 2 \\ 2 & 0 & 3 & 0 & 0 \\ 3 & 3 & 0 & 6 & 0 \\ 7 & 0 & 6 & 0 & 4 \\ 2 & 0 & 0 & 4 & 0 \end{bmatrix}. \tag{8.17}$$

The finding processing of this instance is shown in Fig. 8.10, Initialize the network, set $E[0] = 2.5$ and $\delta E = 1$,

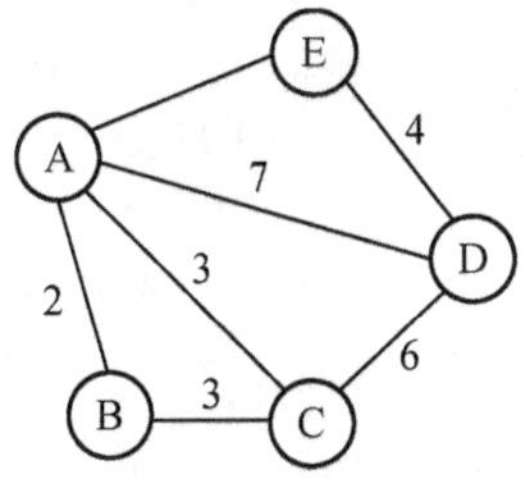

Fig. 8.9. A simple undirected weighted graph

Here, "inf" represents positive infinity. To $U_{ij}[n]$, infinity values will make some fired nodes never fire again. $E[n]$ will be less than the infinity value in $U_{ij}[n]$, so the result makes the fired neurons never fire again. F of the start node is initially set at a infinity value to prevent it from firing again, and $M(i)$ of the start node is set at 1.

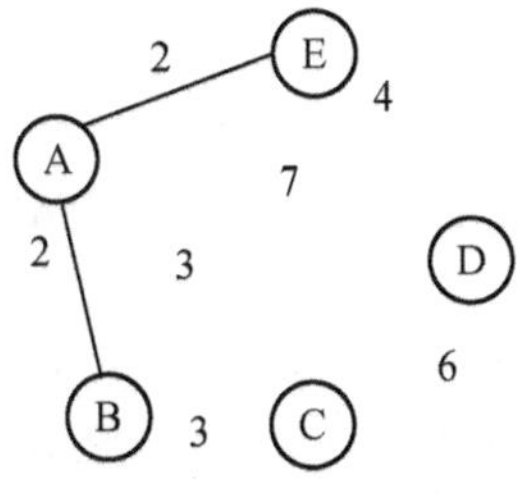

$n=1$, $E=2.5$, $F(5) = (\text{inf}, 2, 0, 0, 2)$,
$M(5) = (1, 1, 0, 0, 1)$

$$U = \begin{bmatrix} 0 & 2 & 3 & 7 & 2 \\ 0 & 0 & 0 & 0 & 0 \\ 0 & 0 & 0 & 0 & 0 \\ 0 & 0 & 0 & 0 & 0 \\ 0 & 0 & 0 & 0 & 0 \end{bmatrix} \qquad Y = \begin{bmatrix} 0 & 1 & 0 & 0 & 1 \\ 0 & 0 & 0 & 0 & 0 \\ 0 & 0 & 0 & 0 & 0 \\ 0 & 0 & 0 & 0 & 0 \\ 0 & 0 & 0 & 0 & 0 \end{bmatrix}$$

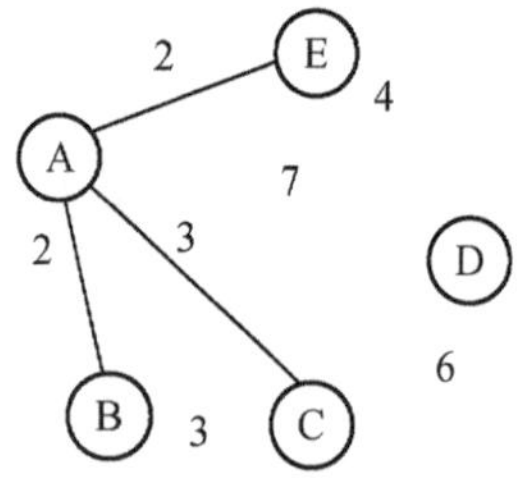

$n=2,\ E=3.5,\ F(5)=(\text{inf},2,3,0,2)$,

$M(5)=(1,1,1,0,1)$

$$U=\begin{bmatrix} 0 & 2 & 3 & 7 & 2 \\ \text{inf} & 0 & 2+3 & 0 & 0 \\ 0 & 0 & 0 & 0 & 0 \\ 0 & 0 & 0 & 0 & 0 \\ \text{inf} & 0 & 0 & 2+4 & 0 \end{bmatrix} \quad Y=\begin{bmatrix} 0 & 1 & 1 & 0 & 1 \\ 0 & 0 & 0 & 0 & 0 \\ 0 & 0 & 0 & 0 & 0 \\ 0 & 0 & 0 & 0 & 0 \\ 0 & 0 & 0 & 0 & 0 \end{bmatrix}$$

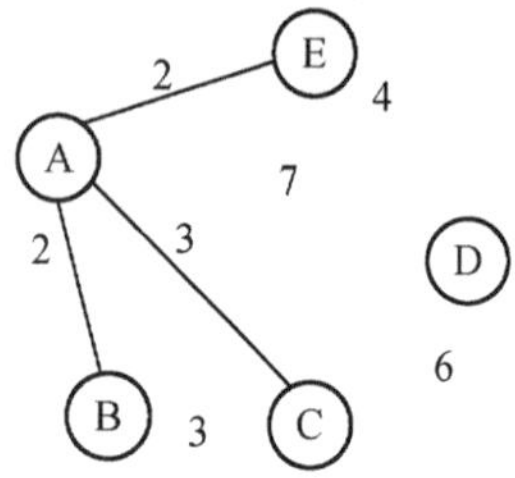

$n=3,\ E=4.5,\ F(5)=(\text{inf},2,3,0,2)$,

$M(5)=(1,1,1,0,1)$

$$U=\begin{bmatrix} 0 & 2 & 3 & 7 & 2 \\ \text{inf} & 0 & 2+3 & 0 & 0 \\ \text{inf} & \text{inf} & 0 & 3+6 & 0 \\ 0 & 0 & 0 & 0 & 0 \\ \text{inf} & 0 & 0 & 2+4 & 0 \end{bmatrix} \quad Y=\begin{bmatrix} 0 & 1 & 1 & 0 & 1 \\ 0 & 0 & 0 & 0 & 0 \\ 0 & 0 & 0 & 0 & 0 \\ 0 & 0 & 0 & 0 & 0 \\ 0 & 0 & 0 & 0 & 0 \end{bmatrix}$$

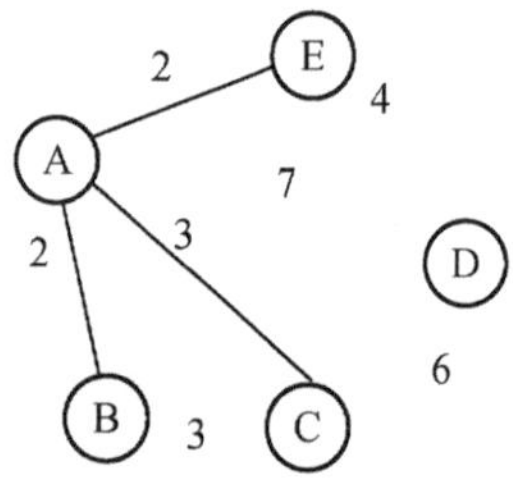

$n=4,\ E=5.5,\ F(5)=(\text{inf},2,3,0,2)$,

$M(5)=(1,1,1,0,1)$

$$U=\begin{bmatrix} 0 & 2 & 3 & 7 & 2 \\ \text{inf} & 0 & 2+3 & 0 & 0 \\ \text{inf} & \text{inf} & 0 & 3+6 & 0 \\ 0 & 0 & 0 & 0 & 0 \\ \text{inf} & 0 & 0 & 2+4 & 0 \end{bmatrix} \quad Y=\begin{bmatrix} 0 & 1 & 1 & 0 & 1 \\ 0 & 0 & 0 & 0 & 0 \\ 0 & 0 & 0 & 0 & 0 \\ 0 & 0 & 0 & 0 & 0 \\ 0 & 0 & 0 & 0 & 0 \end{bmatrix}$$

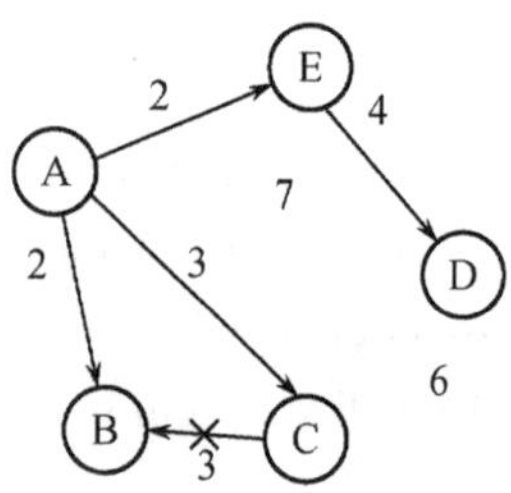

$n=5,\ E=6.5,\ F(5)=(\text{inf},2,3,6,2)$,

$M(5)=(1,1,1,1,1)$

$$U=\begin{bmatrix} 0 & 2 & 3 & 7 & 2 \\ \text{inf} & 0 & 2+3 & 0 & 0 \\ \text{inf} & \text{inf} & 0 & 3+6 & 0 \\ 0 & 0 & 0 & 0 & 0 \\ \text{inf} & 0 & 0 & 2+4 & 0 \end{bmatrix} \quad Y=\begin{bmatrix} 0 & 1 & 1 & 0 & 1 \\ 0 & 0 & 0 & 0 & 0 \\ 0 & 0 & 0 & 0 & 0 \\ 0 & 0 & 0 & 0 & 0 \\ 0 & 0 & 0 & 1 & 0 \end{bmatrix}$$

Fig. 8.10. Finding the shortest path processing of the instance from A to D

8.3.2 Experimental Results and Analysis

The AWNN tries to solve the Traveling Salesman Problem shown in Fig. 8.7. The algorithm for TSP is a little different from SP. With regard to SP, if the wave front reaches the node P, other paths which want to reach P later will stop. However, for TSP, these paths will continue moving forward. TSP is an NP-hard problem. Each candidate path in TSP has its own internal activity

U. So U must be more complex.

Let any node fire first, the output would be the result as shown in Fig. 8.11. The cost is equal to the final route length.

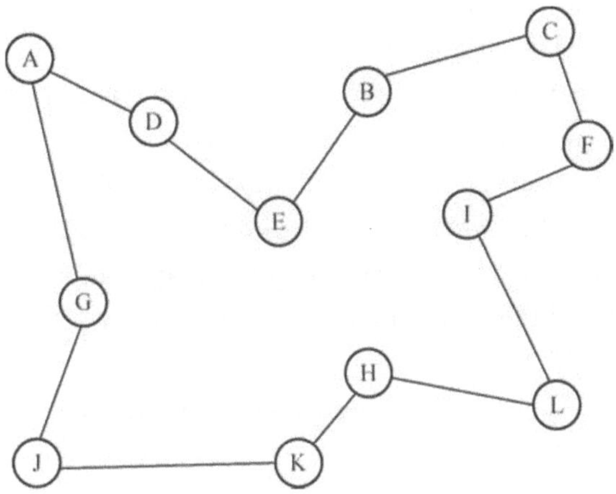

Fig. 8.11. TSP result with AWNN

This section proposes a physiological inspired algorithm, AWNN. It is a robust scheme to solve optimal path problems. AWNN inherits characteristics of parallel processing and auto-wave which are the most important characteristics inspired from physiological neural networks. The two characteristics make AWNN more easily solve the problems. And its cost of optimal path can be determined which is exactly the iterative time.

For computational complexity, the nodes are the pixels in the maze image in Ref. [11]. The PCNN with two-dimensional convolutions made its algorithm very complex, too. The AWNN using adjacency matrix instead of convolutional operation has dramatically decreased the computational complexity.

There are some parts that need to discuss: it can be seen that the AWNN does not perfectly solve the TSP because the possible route numbers are very large, and it takes too much memory during iteration. However, it can be improved by forecasting some impossible paths and eliminating them out of the graph. An alternative idea is to set these impossible paths at the infinite values.

Summary

Combinatorial optimization has been puzzling people for many years. It refers to many foundations such as graph theory and mathematics, and also involves practice method. Translating combinatorial optimization problem into graph or polynomial time algorithm to be solved is an effective passport. This chapter attempts to solve the combinatorial problem with auto-wave feature of the PCNN. With inspiring from neighboring and similar neurons, auto-wave emanated from one neuron propagates through "medium" made up of edges in graph, as the flood visits anywhere in the graph and the path, by which the wave arrives at the destination first, is optimal one.

Obviously, PCNN is potential in combinatorial optimization. There is very wide exploration space in combinatorial optimization.

References

[1] Konigsberg's Bridges Problem. http: //www.contracosta.edu/math/Konig.htm. Accessed 22 February 2009

[2] Ranganath HS, Kuntimad G, Johnson JL (1995) Pulse coupled neural networks for image processing. In: Proceedings of IEEE Southeast Conference, Raleigh, 26 – 29 March 1995

[3] Zhan K, Ma YD, Zhao RC, Feng XW (2009) An efficient algorithm for optimal path problems. Applied Mathematics & Computation (under review)

[4] Eckhorn R, Bauer R, Jordan W et al (1988) Coherent oscillations: a mechanism of feature linking in the visual cortex? Multiple electrode and correlation analyses in the cat. Biological Cybernetics 12(60): 121 – 130

[5] Eckhorn R, Reitboeck HJ, Arndt M et al (1989) Feature linking via stimulus-evoked oscillations: experimental results from cat visual cortex and functional implications from a network model. Neural Networks 6(1): 723 – 730

[6] Eckhorn R, Reitboeck HJ, Arndt M et al (1990) Feature linking via synchronization among distributed assemblies: simulation of results from cat cortex. Neural Computation 2(3): 293 – 307

[7] Ma YD, Dai RL, Li L (2002) Image segmentation of embryonic plant cell using pulse-coupled neural networks. Chinese Science Bulletin 47(2): 167 – 172

[8] Zhang JW, Zhan K, Ma YD (2007) Rotation and scale invariant antinoise PCNN features for content-based image retrieval. Neural Network World 17(2): 121 – 132

[9] Xu GZ, Zhang ZF, Ma YD (2008) a novel method for iris feature extraction based on interesting cortical model network. Journal of Applied Mathematics & Computing 26(1): 341 – 352

[10] Wang ZB, Ma YD, Cheng FY, Yang LZ (2010) Review of Pulse Coupled Neural Networks. Image and Vision Computing 28(1): 5 – 13

[11] Caulfield HJ, Kinser JM (1999) Finding the shortest path in the shortest time using PCNNs. IEEE Transactions on Neural Networks 10(3): 604 – 606

[12] Hong Q, Zhang Y (2007) A new algorithm for finding the shortest paths using PCNN. Chaos, Solitons & Fractals 33(4): 1220 – 1229

[13] Zhao RC, Ma YD, Zhan K (2008) Three-state cascading pulse coupled neural network and the application in finding shortest paths. Systems Engineering and Electronics 30(9): 1785 – 1789

Chapter 9 FPGA Implementation of PCNN Algorithm

The PCNN image processing algorithms are generally programmed on PC platform [1, 2]. These algorithms have fully demonstrated their outstanding performance. With the development of large-scale integrated circuit technology, the hardware implementation of neural network becomes more and more imperative. The combination of the DSP, FPGA (Field-Programmable Gate Array) and other hardware with neural network provides a standout platform for further research and application of neural network information processing. This chapter will discuss the FPGA implementation of the PCNN image processing algorithm.

9.1 Fundamental Principle of PCNN Hardware Implementation

Chua and Yang originated the cellular neural networks (CNN) in 1988 [3]. It is a large-scale nonlinear analog circuit, which can achieve real-time, high-speed parallel signal processing. One advantage of the CNN is easy to be implemented by the VLSI. The core of the CNN is shown in Fig. 9.1, which consists of linear resistance, linear capacitors and voltage-controlled current sources. A unit is corresponding to a neuron which is actually a first order nonlinear circuit. Nowadays the hardware-based CNN model has already been used in image processing [4].

Traditionally, a neuron is implemented through the CMOS-based analog circuit unit. Johnson proposed a PCNN chip model, which has eight units per row under 1MHz operating frequency [5]. Padgett also designed a CMOS-based analog circuit of the PCNN [6]. Kinser et al. implemented the complex

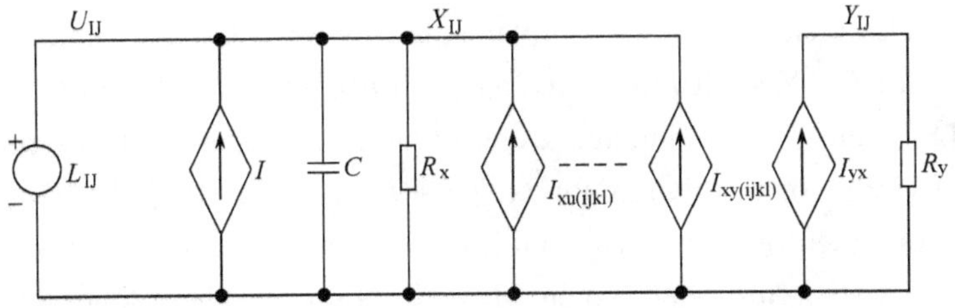

Fig. 9.1. Core of cellular neural networks

structure of PCNN model with CMOS-based analog circuit unit [7]. Compared with the PC simulation, the speed of PCNN processing on hardware platform is much faster. However, a neuron corresponds to a pixel in the application of image processing, which leads to the requirement of amount of hardware resources. At the same time, the complex settings of its parameters limit its hardware implementation.

Therefore, there are some references exclusively focused on hardware platform design of the PCNN. Chacon et al. proposed the conception of the PCNN processor and designed a user interface which can realize the settings of parameters [8]. The CNAPS processor proposed in Ref. [9] made the direct parallel architecture of the PCNN come true. The structure of the CNAPS is shown in Fig. 9.2. It uses the expansion card with architecture of the Single Instruction Multiple Data (SIMD) made by the Adaptive Solutions Company. Although the CNAPS processor made the hardware implementation of the PCNN easier, it is not a general parallel computer architecture model [10]. So the scale of its application is limited.

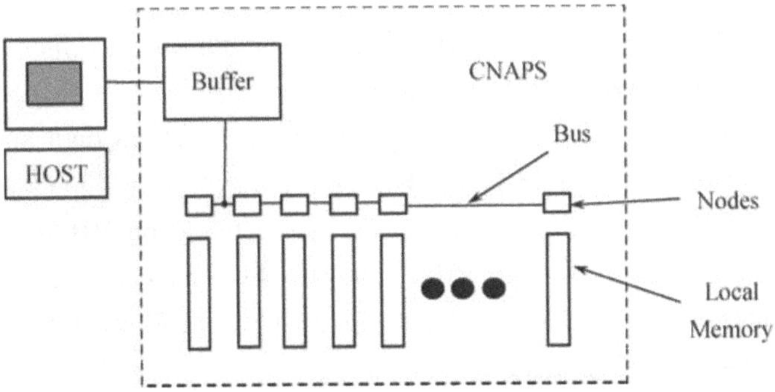

Fig. 9.2. Schematic drawing of CNAPS [9]

Nowadays, the PCNN was implemented by Very Large Scale Integrated Circuit (VLSI). Yasuhiro suggested a circuit organization of the PCNN using the VLSI, which was used in image denoising [11]. Matolin et al. also proposed a VLSI circuit of the PCNN for image segmentation [12]. The photodiode scheme designed by Guest [13] could implement some basic functions of the PCNN. Its structure is shown in Fig. 9.3. However, these kinds of circuit models only consisted of diodes and CMOS devices, which limited some of their application fields. Under some special circumstances, it is necessary to preprocess directly the data from input of leading end intelligent sensor by the PCNN. Some integrated circuits (LAPP1100, 1510, and MAPP2200) [14, 15] were designed to finish this task.

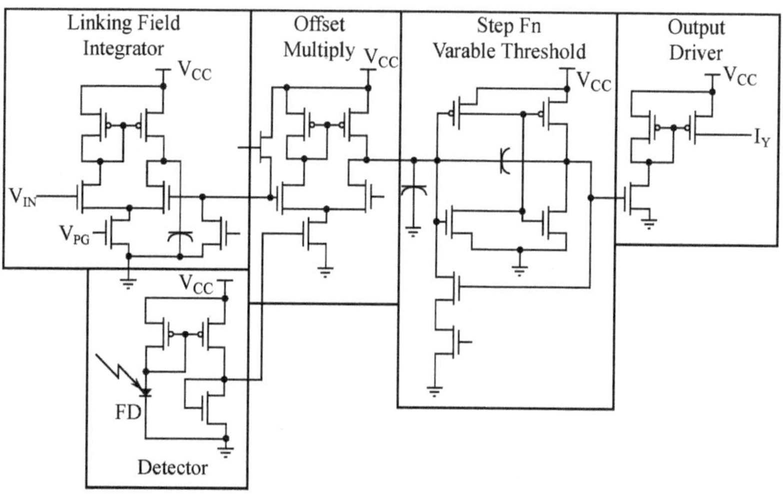

Fig. 9.3. PCNN circuit model implemented by photodiodes [13]

Due to PCNN's complex calculations, its simulation is difficult to meet the real-time requirements. Nevertheless, it is feasible to implement PCNN on FPGA because of its outstanding advantages such as high speed, easy implementation, and plenty of RAMs.

Waldemark et al. proposed a PCNN model based on VHDL [16]. Each neuron's input was 8-bit gray value and the size of its linking matrix was 3×3. The model cost 22% of the logic cells of Altera Flex10K100 chip, and its operating frequency was a little over 4 MHz.

Another VHDL-based PCNN algorithm was given in Ref. [17]. It can process sixty 128×128 images per second while the iterative number of each image was 70. Besides, the system is capable of adjusting PCNN parameters automatically. 290 I/O pins of Altera Flex10K250 chip were occupied and the system frequency was 70 MHz. In each iteration, the model added a delay buffer. All parameters of the PCNN were divided into integer and fractional parts to ensure the precision.

Recently, Vega-Pineda et al. proposed an FPGA system of PCNN and successfully applied it into image sequence processing [18]. It could process 250M pixels per second, so real-time image processing would be easily implemented.

9.2 Altera DE2-70 Implementation of PCNN

When implementing the PCNN on the FPGA, the output signal is determined by both current state and previous state. So the system is designed with sequential logical circuit.

Synchronization circuit is used here to avoid delay of design and errors of system because asynchronous circuit is more apt to produce competition and risk.

The PCNN model described by Eqs.(1.11)–(1.15) is adopted to implement the maximum-entropy based image segmentation algorithm in this section. It will cost too much resources of the FPGA chip, especially for high-resolution images because of a neuron corresponding to a pixel.

In this section the neuron is recycled in order to avoid this kind of waste and the dual port RAM of FPGA is used to store the processed pixels. At the same time, different counters are designed to read corresponding pixel values, respectively.

As shown in Fig. 9.4, set a label matrix B to record the states of pixels. The value in B will be set at 1 when the corresponding pixel is activated and at 0 when it is not. Note that all pixels will be activated in the first iteration, but B is still kept unchanged in this iteration.

In the second iteration, activation of the pixel only depends on its value and its corresponding threshold. When the threshold exponentially decays to the maximal pixel value, it will be activated. Then corresponding value in B is set at 1, the threshold of activated pixel will be set at a larger value to avoid being activated immediately again. With the increment of iterative number,

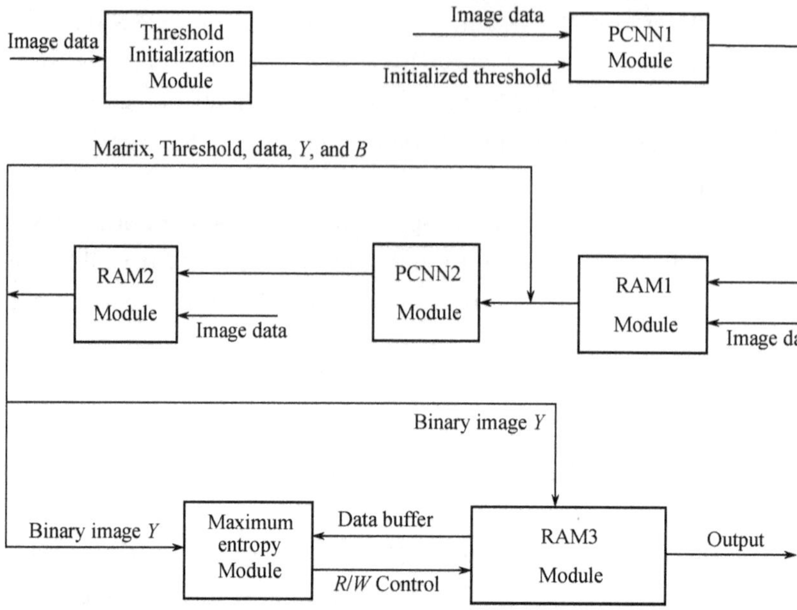

Fig. 9.4. Module diagram of PCNN system based on FPGA

the threshold decays exponentially. When the dynamic threshold meets the pixel value (the value is affected by surrounding activated pixels), it will be activated.

In fact, two PCNN modules are designed to accomplish these processes. The first one is designed for the second iteration. The second one is used when the iterative number is greater than two. In the second module, the pixel compared with the threshold is not the pixel value of the input image only, but a new value affected by both itself and surrounding pixels.

QuartusII, NiosII, Sopc Builder and other software of Altera have provided rich library functions and the solutions of interaction between hardware and software, which makes the PCNN algorithm easier to be implemented by FPGA. Verilog HDL language is used to implement all modules.

Altera CycloneII 2C70 FPGA has 70 000 logical modules and 250 M4K (4Kbit+512 bit parity check code), which can increase the flexibility of design and satisfy the requirements of buffer memories; there are complete FPGA hardware development environment and NiosII IDE software development environment in Altera QuartusII. It will make the designer possible to build the overall system easily; it has rich peripheral interfaces which could offer a variety of options of design.

9.2.1 PCNN Implementation Using Altera DE2-70 [19]

The capacity of each dual port RAM is 4096 × 8 bits in Altera DE2-70. A PCNN hardware system based on Altera DE2-70 is designed in this section, which can process gray image with 64 × 64 × 8 bits. 10 dual port RAMs are designed to store gray value of input image, threshold, label matrix B, and output image.

The module diagram of the PCNN system based on the FPGA is shown in Fig. 9.4. The RAM1 module and the RAM2 module include four dual-port RAMs, respectively. These RAMs store input data, threshold, label matrix B, and binary image Y. The RAM3 module consists of two dual port RAMs (data buffer RAM and output image RAM) and stores optimally segmented image. The threshold initialization module is to generate initialized threshold according to pixel value of input image. The task of the PCNN1 module is to complete the second iteration of the PCNN. And the PCNN2 module is responsible for further iteration. Maximum entropy is employed to evaluate the quality of binary image [20]. Maximum entropy module judges the entropy of output binary image. The binary image with maximum entropy is stored in the RAM3. It is the optimally segmented image.

The detailed processes will be described as follows:

Input image is firstly processed by the threshold initialization module and the initialized threshold is obtained by an adaptive algorithm. And then the PCNN1 module, being affected by the initialized threshold and input image, produces threshold matrix, label matrix B, and binary image Y in the second iteration. These matrixes are stored in the RAM1. In subsequent iteration, the PCNN2 module uses surrounding neurons' output, threshold, and label matrix B which are generated in the PCNN1 module (in the 3rd iteration) or PCNN2 itself (others) to decide whether the current neuron will be activated. In the process of iteration, the maximum entropy module always computes the entropy of Y produced by the PCNN2 module until maximum entropy is found. Image with maximum entropy is obtained when PCNN stops.

In Fig. 9.4, the adaptive threshold algorithm is adopted in the threshold initialization module. The interval [0, 255] of gray value is divided into 26 sub-intervals whose lengths are 10. The distribution of the gray value of input image is counted in those sub-intervals. When the largest probability is found in one sub-interval, the minimum pixel gray value of this sub-interval is just the initialized threshold.

In this system, the iterative number of the PCNN is converted into the number of cycles between the RAM2 and the PCNN2. The duty-cycle operation between the PCNN2 and the RAM2 saves hardware resources while maximum entropy module realizes automatic segmentation with less man-made operations and also makes the system more intellectualized.

Maximum entropy is calculated with Eq. (9.1), where $H(p)$ denotes the entropy of binary image; p_0 and p_1 represent the probability of 0 and 1 in Y.

$$H(p) = -p_0 \log_2 p_0 - p_1 \log_2 p_1. \tag{9.1}$$

In order to implement easily in verilog HDL, it is necessary to convert Eq. (9.1) to Eq. (9.2).

$$\begin{aligned} 2^{H(p)} &= 2^{-p_0 \log_2 p_0 - p_1 \log_2 p_1} \\ &= 2^{\log_2 (p_0^{-p_0} p_1^{-p_1})} \\ &= p_0^{-p_0} p_1^{-p_1} \\ &= (p_0^{p_0} p_1^{p_1})^{-1}. \end{aligned} \tag{9.2}$$

For the binary image Y,

$$p_1 = \frac{x}{N}, p_0 = \frac{N-x}{N}, \tag{9.3}$$

where, N denotes the number of all pixels in Y; x denotes the number of 1 in Y.

Hence,

$$p_0^{p_0} p_1^{p_1} = \left(\frac{N-x}{N}\right)^{\frac{N-x}{N}} \left(\frac{x}{N}\right)^{\frac{x}{N}}. \tag{9.4}$$

If the minimum of $p_0^{p_0} p_1^{p_1}$ is found, then maximum entropy $H(p)$ is obtained.

In addition, the PCNN2 module contains an iteration control module. The iterative number is set empirically to a predefined value at the beginning. When it reaches the predefined value, the iteration control module sets clk_odd=0 in the PCNN2 module and ends the iterations.

There are four main modules in Fig. 9.4: serial-in-parallel-out module, PCNN module, threshold initialization module, and maximum entropy module.

1) Serial-in-parallel-out module

This module changes the input serial data into 8 parallel output with 8 bit data. As shown in Fig. 9.5(a), output has two parts which should be out0 − out3 and out4 − out7. When the next clock arrives, data in out0 − out3 are transferred to out4 − out7. Its simulation is shown in Fig. 9.5(b).

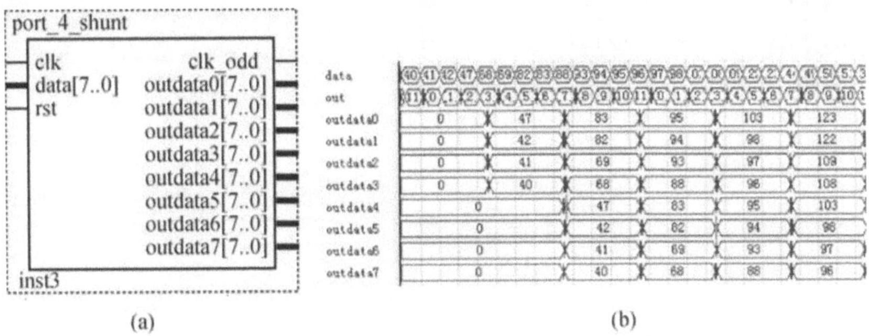

Fig. 9.5. Serial-in-parallel-out module. (a) hardware modules, (b) timing simulation

2) PCNN module

The PCNN1 module and PCNN2 module are shown in Figs. 9.6(a) and (b) respectively. Fig. 9.6(c) is the internal structure of the PCNN2 module.

In the PCNN1 module, U[7..0] is the serial input image data. Threshold1[7..0] is the initial threshold. Nn[3..0] is a control port. Out1[7..0] is its

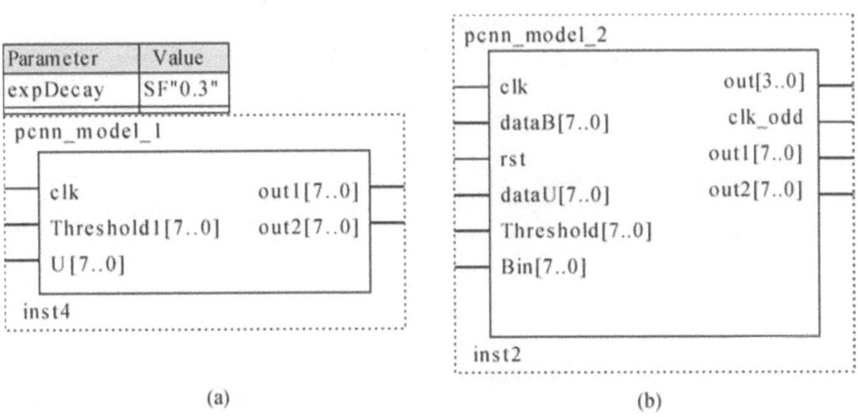

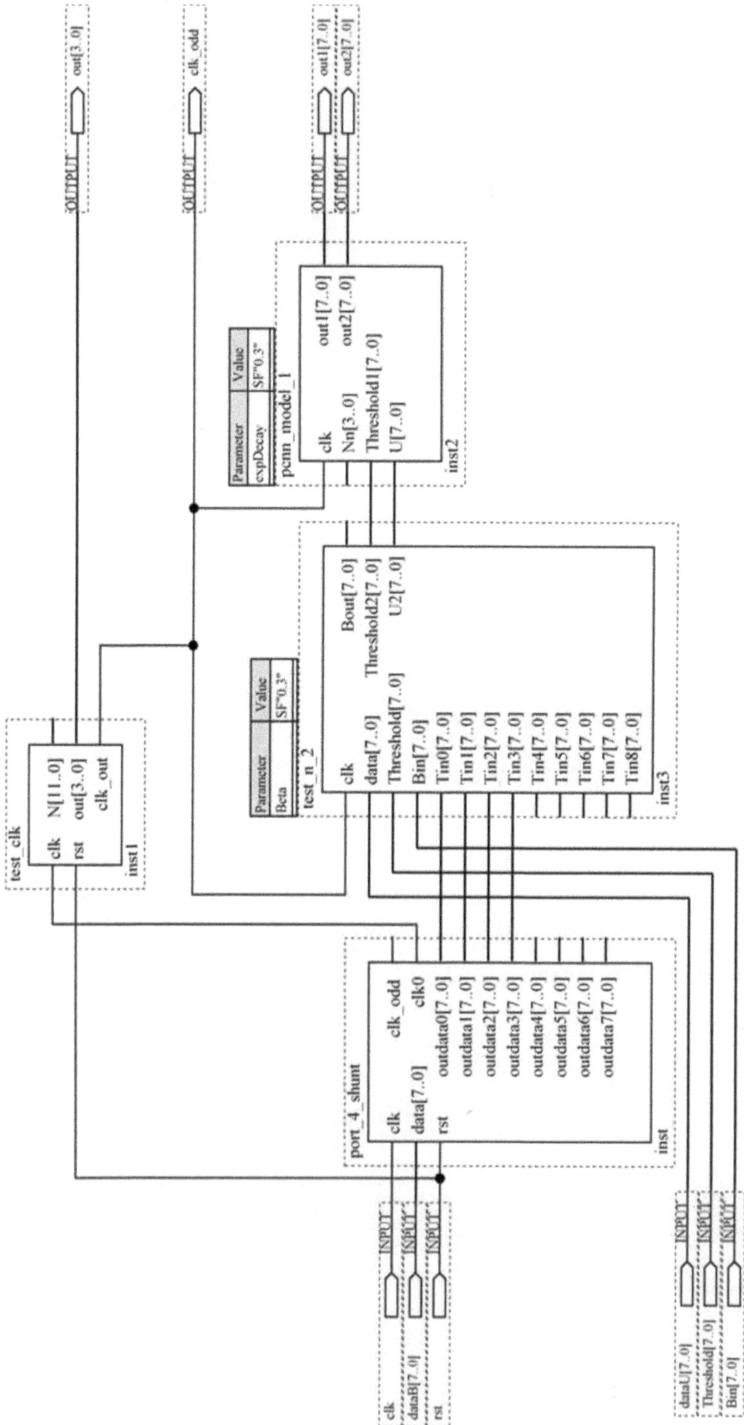

(c)

Fig. 9.6. PCNN module:(a) PCNN1 module, (b) PCNN2 module, (c) the internal structure of PCNN2 module

threshold output. Out2[7..0] is its label matrix output.

In the PCNN2 module, dataB[7..0] is the linking matrix with size 3×3. DataU[7..0] is the image data input, threshold[7..0] is the threshold produced in the PCNN1 module. Bin[7..0] is the label matrix B. Out1[7..0] is its threshold output and out2[7..0] is its label matrix output. Out[3..0] is the number of iterations.

3) Threshold initialization module

It generates the initial threshold for the PCNN1 module. In Fig. 9.7(a), data[7..0] is the input image data. Threshold[11..0] is the threshold output, and the control port controls reading/writing of the RAM1. K[31..0] is a counter that is used to count the number of input data. The timing sequence simulation diagram is shown in Fig. 9.7(b). Here the example of the initialized threshold is 40 when the maximal probability of pixel value happens between 40 and 50.

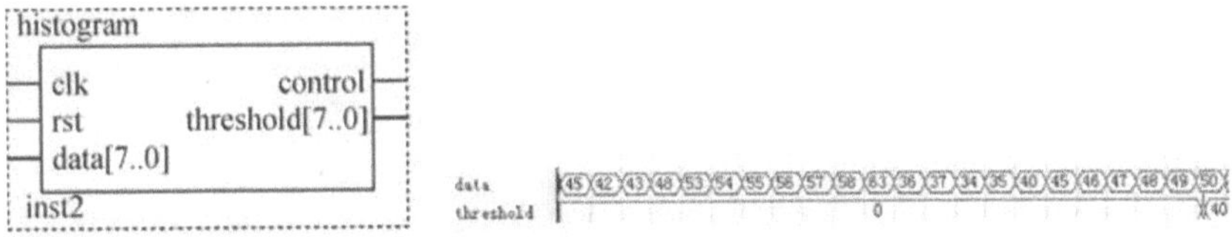

(a) (b)

Fig. 9.7. Threshold initialization module: (a) hardware modules, (b) timing sequence simulation

4) Maximum entropy module

It judges whether binary image Y is the optimally segmented image.

In Fig. 9.8(a), N[3..0] is the iterative number. Data[7..0] is the binary image Y. The control port controls reading/writing of the RAM3. The module calculates maximum entropy of input values. When the entropy is the maximal one, the binary image Y is the optimally segmented image and control port is set at 1. Then the optimally segmented image is written into the RAM3. The internal structure of maximum entropy module is shown in Fig. 9.8(b). Maximum entropy module computes the maximum entropy of Y and store module stores the entropy. Judge module judges whether the control port is 1 or 0.

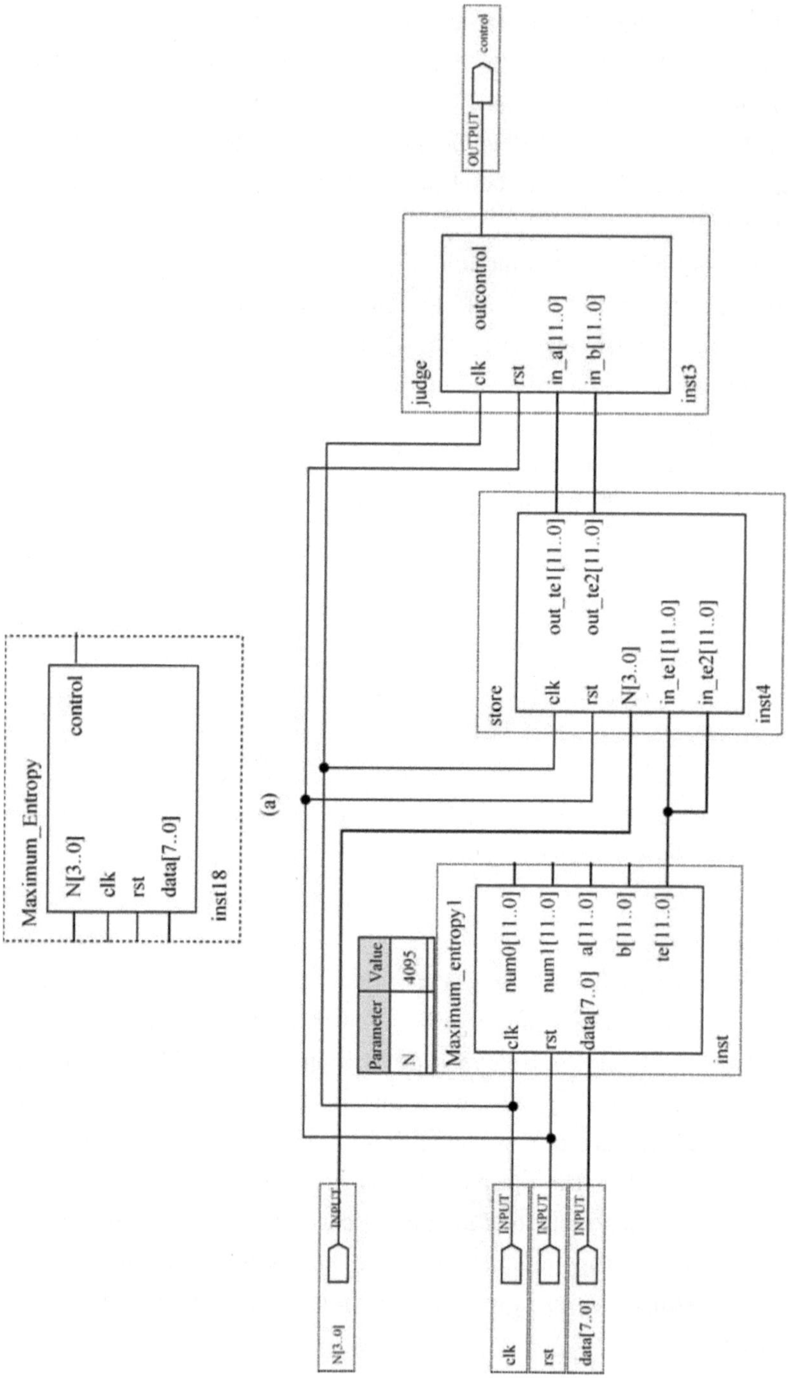

Fig. 9.8. Maximum entropy module: (a) hardware modules; (b) the internal struc ture of maximum entropy module

9.2.2 Experimental Results and Analysis

1) The settings of parameters in the PCNN module

With the investigation on many experiments, the parameters of the PCNN model are set empirically, and shown in Table 9.1. To avoid the over-segmentation of the rich detailed images, the total iterative number is set at 10.

Table 9.1. Parameters used in the PCNN algorithm.

parameters	V_E	V_F	β	α_L	α_F	α_E	V_L
value	0	0	0.3	∞	∞	0.3	1

And its linking matrix is set to be: $W = \begin{bmatrix} 0, & 1, & 0 \\ 1, & 0, & 1 \\ 0, & 1, & 0 \end{bmatrix}$.

2) Power consumption, clock frequency, and resource occupation

The resource occupation information of this system is shown in Fig. 9.9.

Quartus II Version	8.0 Build 215 05/29/2008 SJ Web Edition
Revision Name	T_PCNN
Top-level Entity Name	T_PCNN
Family	Cyclone II
Device	EP2C70F896C6
Timing Models	Final
Met timing requirements	No
Total logic elements	1,625/68,416 (2 %)
Total combinational functions	1,592/68,416 (2 %)
Dedicated logic registers	431/68,416 (<1 %)
Total registers	431
Total pins	22/622 (4%)
Total virtual pins	0
Total memory bits	360, 448/1, 152, 000 (31 %)
Embedded Multiplier 9-bit elements	2/300 (<1 %)
Total PLLs	0/4 (0 %)

Fig. 9.9. The resource occupation information of the system.

The proposed algorithm occupies about 2% logic units of the Altera Cyclone II EP2C70F896C6 chip and 31% capacity of its internal RAM. The system processes data at the frequency of 283 MHz. For segmenting a 64×64 image, it costs only 1.25ms, but the simulation costs 0.83s on MATLAB platform (P_4 2.8GHZ/1GDDR-ram).

3) Analysis of some Experiments

To show the superiority of hardware implementation, the segmented image is compared with the one on MATLAB simulation under the same parameters in Table.9.1.

Six images (Cameraman, Blood, Lena, Man, Cell, and Tire) are used in the experiments. Their size is $64 \times 64 \times 8$ bits. According to their distribution characteristics of histogram as shown in Fig. 9.10, six images can be divided into three groups: Cameraman & Blood, Lena & Man, and Cell & Tire. The thresholds are automatically produced by the initialization module in Figs. 9.14, 9.18, 9.22, 9.26, 9.30, and 9.34. In addition, the initial threshold is set manually in Figs. 9.11–9.13, Figs. 9.15–9.17, Figs. 9.19–9.21, Figs. 9.23–9.25, Figs. 9.27–9.29, and Figs. 9.31–9.33, respectively. The results implemented on FPGA are shown in the first rows. And the simulation results implemented on MATLAB are shown in the second rows in Figs. 9.11–9.34.

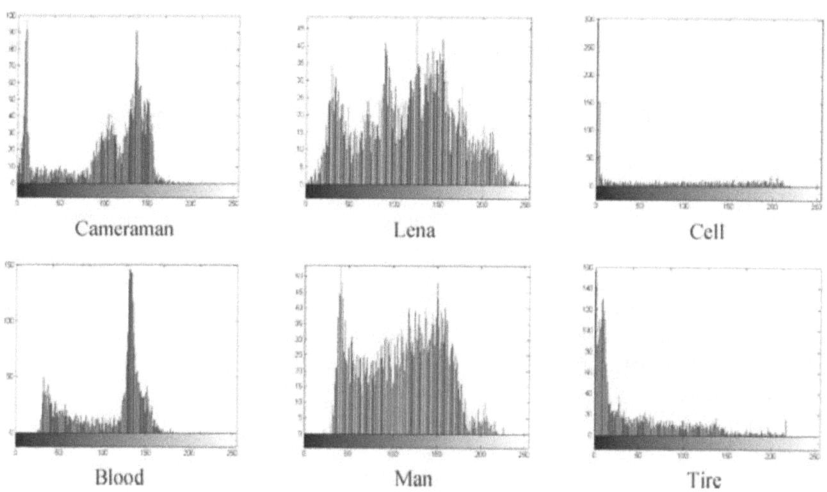

Fig. 9.10. Histograms of six images

It is clear that the segmentation results of Cameraman in Fig. 9.11 are poor when $T_0 = 50$; the results in Fig. 9.12 are litter better improvement when $T_0 = 120$; the results in Fig. 9.13 are good when $T_0 = 143$. Furthermore, the segmentation results in Fig. 9.14 are best when the initial threshold value is set automatically, and its value will be 150.

Hence, the segmented image will obtain much more details of objects and background, it will be better when the threshold value is changed manually from 50, 100 to 143. When $T_0 = 143$, the segmented image includes most of

(a) Original image (b) N=1, $H(P)$=0.79 (c) N=4, $H(P)$=0.74 (d) N=5, $H(P)$=0.73 (e) N=7, $H(P)$=0.71

Fig. 9.11. Results of Cameraman with manually initialized threshold ($T_0 = 50$)

(a) Original image (b) N=1, $H(P)$=0.97 (c) N=4, $H(P)$=0.84 (d) N=5, $H(P)$=0.83 (e) N=7, $H(P)$=0.81

Fig. 9.12. Results of Cameraman with manually initialized threshold ($T_0 = 120$)

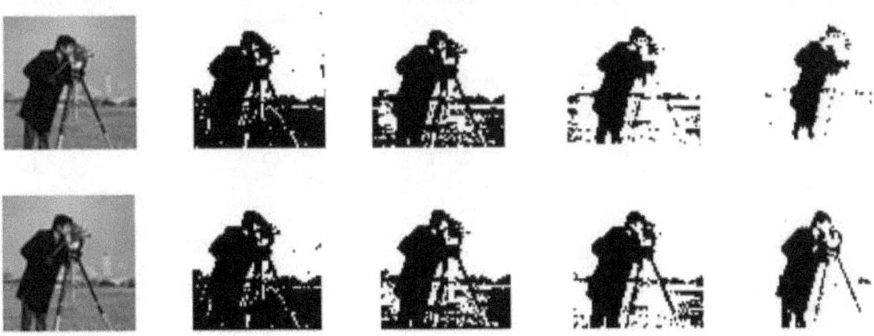

(a) Original image (b) N=1, $H(P)$=0.96 (c) N=4, $H(P)$=0.99 (d) N=5, $H(P)$=0.85 (e) N=7, $H(P)$=0.83

Fig. 9.13. Results of Cameraman with manually initialized threshold ($T_0 = 143$)

details and is very close to 150 which is obtained according to the automatically initialized threshold.

Some similar results have been obtained for Lena, Blood cell and Man. They are shown in Figs. 9.15–9.18, Figs. 9.19–9.22, and Figs. 9.23–9.26, respectively.

(a) Original image (b) N=3, $H(P)$=0.87 (c) N=4, $H(P)$=0.99 (d) N=5, $H(P)$=0.78 (e) N=7, $H(P)$=0.67

Fig. 9.14. Results of Cameraman with automatically initialized threshold ($T_0 = 150$)

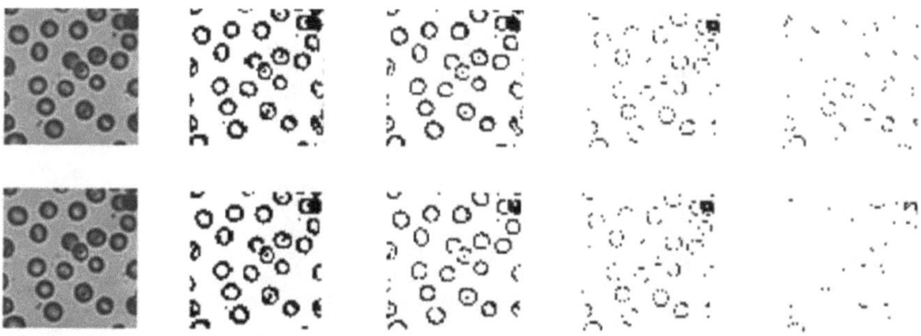

(a) Original image (b) N=1, $H(P)$=0.79 (c) N=4, $H(P)$=0.41 (d) N=5, $H(P)$=0.21 (e) N=7, $H(P)$=0.20

Fig. 9.15. Results of Blood with manually initialized threshold ($T_0 = 70$)

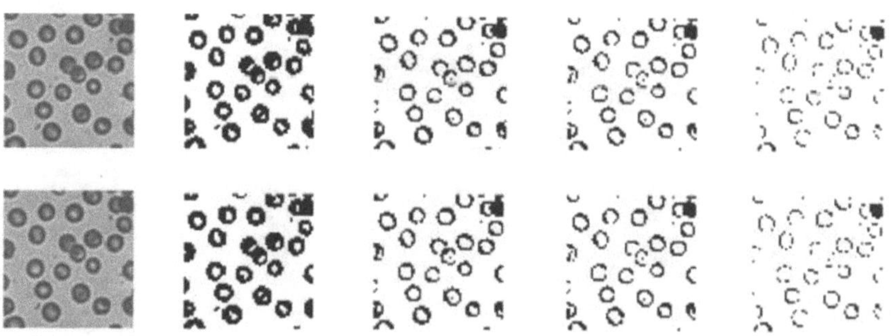

(a) Original image (b) N=1, $H(P)$=0.90 (c) N=4, $H(P)$=0.72 (d) N=5, $H(P)$=0.66 (e) N=7, $H(P)$=0.49

Fig. 9.16. Results of Blood with manually initialized threshold ($T_0 = 100$)

Some experimental results of segmentation are explored in detail as bellows when the initial threshold value will be set manually. Here let T_0 denote the initial threshold in the following statement.

For the first two groups (Cameraman & Blood and Lena & Man), the

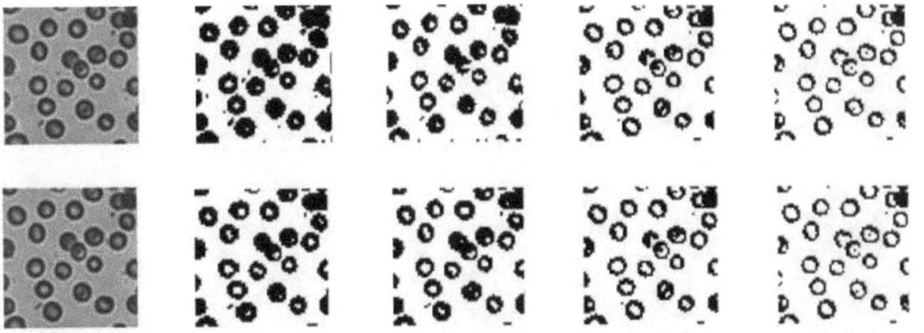

(a) Original image (b) N=1, $H(P)$=0.90 (c) N=3, $H(P)$=0.99 (d) N=5, $H(P)$=0.83 (e) N=7, $H(P)$=0.74

Fig. 9.17. Results of Blood with manually initialized threshold ($T_0 = 140$)

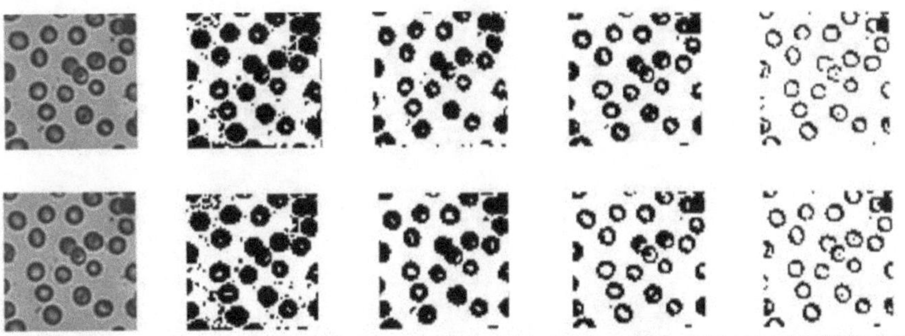

(a) Original image (b) N=1, $H(P)$=0.92 (c) N=3, $H(P)$=0.99 (d) N=5, $H(P)$=0.86 (e) N=7, $H(P)$=0.67

Fig. 9.18. Results of Blood images with automatically initialized threshold ($T_0 = 150$)

(a) Original image (b) N=1, $H(P)$=0.69 (c) N=4, $H(P)$=0.44 (d) N=5, $H(P)$=0.34 (e) N=7, $H(P)$=0.27

Fig. 9.19. Results of Lena with manually initialized threshold ($T_0 = 50$)

optimally segmented images are obtained with the automatically initialized threshold and Maximum entropy rule. However, for the last group (Cell & Tire) the experiment results are very different. It will be illustrated as bellows.

For Cell image, the segmentation results in Fig. 9.27 are poor when $T_0 =$

(a) Original image (b) N=1, $H(P)$=0.97 (c) N=4, $H(P)$=0.76 (d) N=5, $H(P)$=0.72 (e) N=7, $H(P)$=0.66

Fig. 9.20. Results of Lena with manually initialized threshold ($T_0 = 100$)

(a) Original image (b) N=3, $H(P)$=0.82 (c) N=4, $H(P)$=0.99 (d) N=5, $H(P)$=0.77 (e) N=6, $H(P)$=0.72

Fig. 9.21. Results of Lena with manually initialized threshold ($T_0 = 150$)

(a) Original image (b) N=3, $H(P)$=0.71 (c) N=4, $H(P)$=0.99 (d) N=5, $H(P)$=0.66 (e) N=6, $H(P)$=0.55

Fig. 9.22. Results of Lena images with automatically initialized threshold ($T_0 = 160$)

80; the results in Fig. 9.28 are a little better when $T_0 = 100$; the results in Fig. 9.29 are good when $T_0 = 150$. However, the results in Fig. 9.30 are not the best ones when T_0 is automatically initialized, and it is 10. It is shown that threshold initialization module cannot produce the proper value. Similar

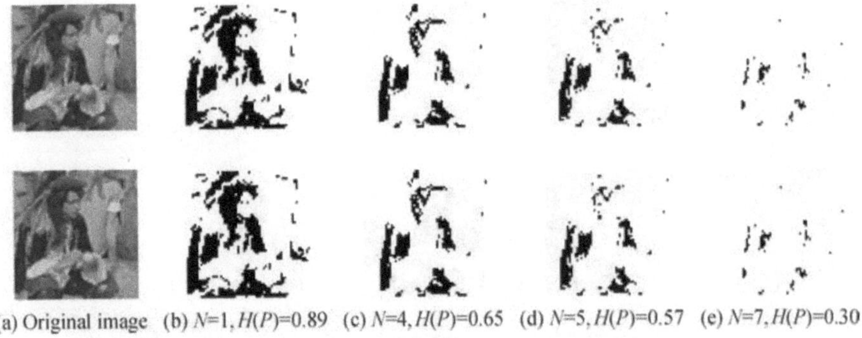

Fig. 9.23. Results of Man with manually initialized threshold ($T_0 = 80$)

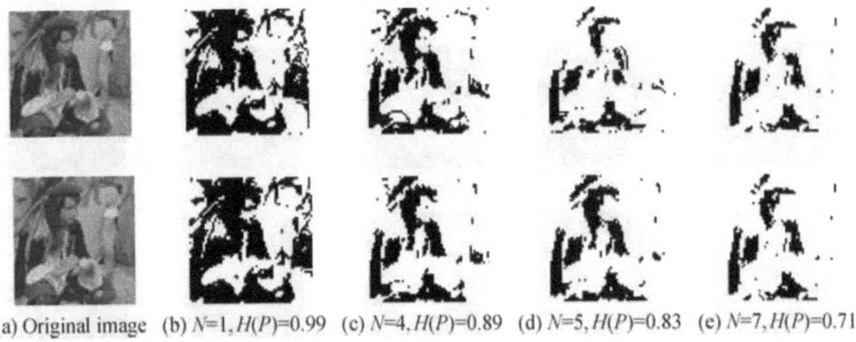

Fig. 9.24. Results of Man with manually initialized threshold ($T_0 = 80$)

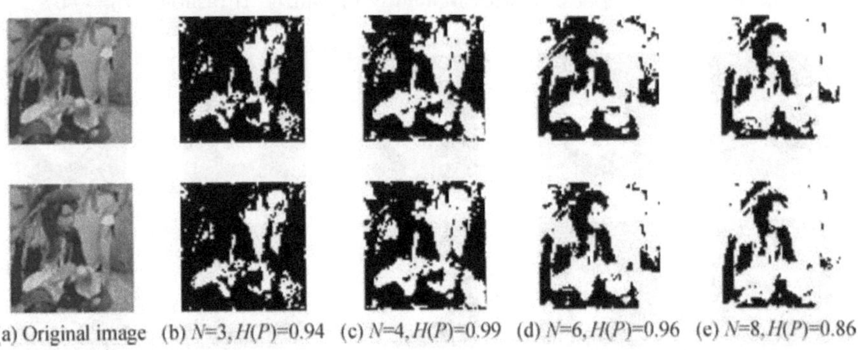

Fig. 9.25. Results of Man with manually initialized threshold ($T_0 = 170$)

experimental results, shown in Figs. 9.31 – 9.34, have been obtained for Tire image.

As shown in Fig. 9.29, the segmentation results of Cell are the best ones when $T_0 = 150$. It should be noticed that at the same time, as shown in Fig. 9.30, when the initial threshold value is set automatically, its value will be 10.

(a) Original image (b) N=1, $H(P)$=0.76 (c) N=3, $H(P)$=0.99 (d) N=6, $H(P)$=0.90 (e) N=8, $H(P)$=0.79

Fig. 9.26. Results of Man images with automatically initialized threshold ($T_0 = 150$)

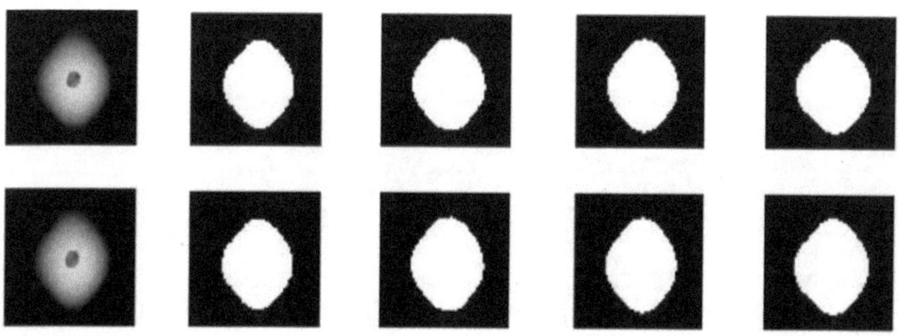

(a) Original image (b) N=1, $H(P)$=0.80 (c) N=4, $H(P)$=0.83 (d) N=5, $H(P)$=0.84 (e) N=7, $H(P)$=0.85

Fig. 9.27. Results of Cell with manually initialized threshold ($T_0 = 80$)

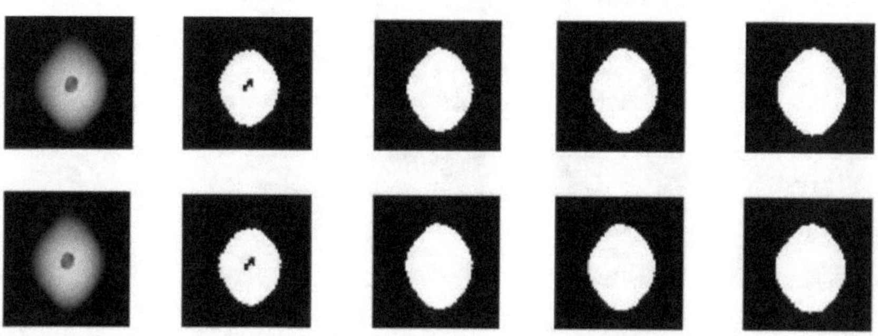

(a) Original image (b) N=1, $H(P)$=0.70 (c) N=4, $H(P)$=0.78 (d) N=5, $H(P)$=0.79 (e) N=7, $H(P)$=0.81

Fig. 9.28. Results of Cell with manually initialized threshold ($T_0 = 100$)

It is very different from 150, the value manually set. And the segmentation results of Cell are very poor, not the best ones as expected.

Obviously, it means that the segmented image with threshold set manually is good one but the one with threshold set automatically is not the one

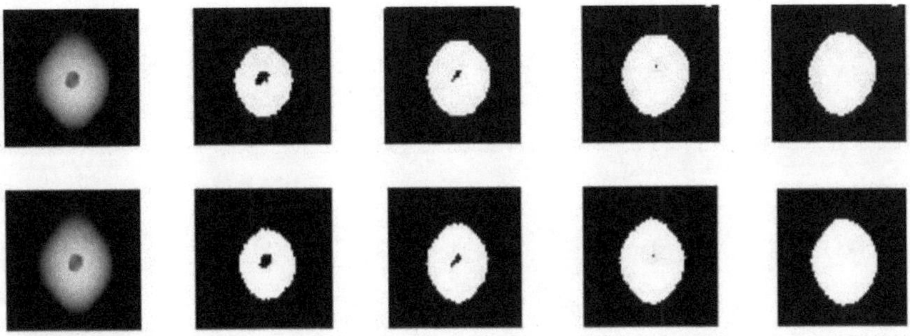

(a) Original image (b) N=4, $H(P)$=0.82 (c) N=5, $H(P)$=0.84 (d) N=6, $H(P)$=0.85 (e) N=7, $H(P)$=0.87

Fig. 9.29. Results of Cell with manually initialized threshold ($T_0 = 150$)

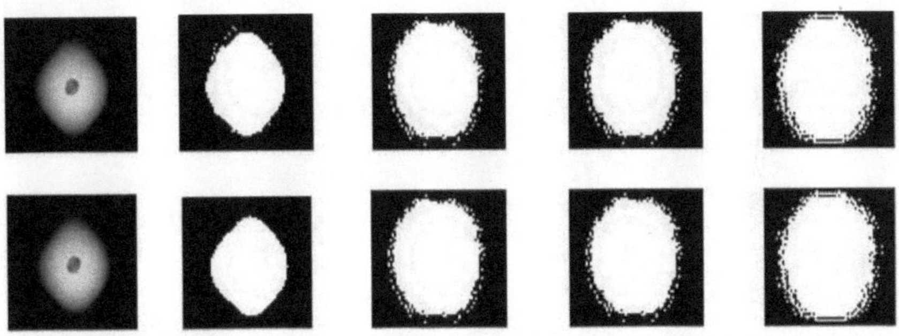

(a) Original image (b) N=1, $H(P)$=0.91 (c) N=4, $H(P)$=0.997 (d) N=5, $H(P)$=0.998 (e) N=6, $H(P)$=0.993

Fig. 9.30. Results of Cell images with automatically initialized threshold ($T_0 = 10$)

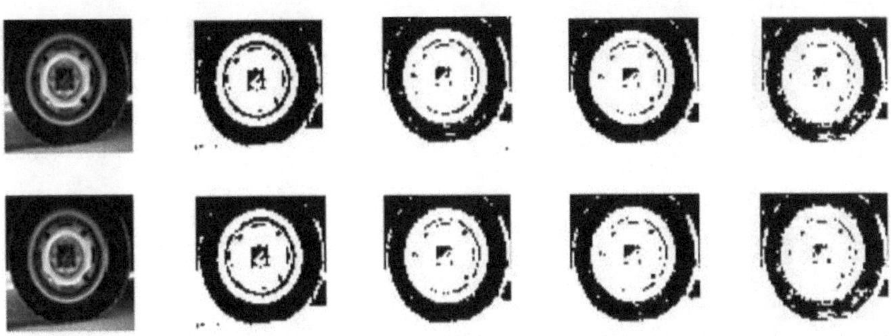

(a) Original image (b) N=1, $H(P)$=0.987 (c) N=4, $H(P)$=1.00 (d) N=5, $H(P)$=0.999 (e) N=7, $H(P)$=0.991

Fig. 9.31. Results of Tire with manually initialized threshold ($T_0 = 30$)

expected as usual.

However, for the last group Cell & Tire as shown in Figs. 9.30(d) and 9.34(b), the final output image is obtained at $N_{max} = 5$ for Cell and its maximum entropy $H(P) = 0.998$, and for Tire the final output image is obtained at $N_{max} = 1$ and its maximum entropy $H(P) = 0.92$. But actually

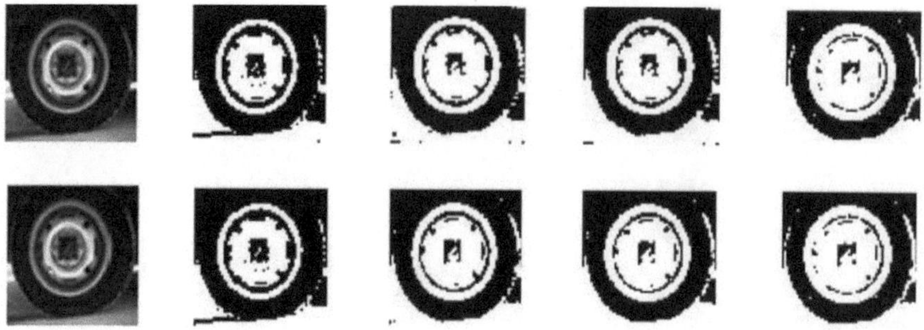

(a) Original image (b) N=1, $H(P)$=0.933 (c) N=4, $H(P)$=0.985 (d) N=5, $H(P)$=0.995 (e) N=7, $H(P)$=0.998

Fig. 9.32. Results of Tire with manually initialized threshold ($T_0 = 30$)

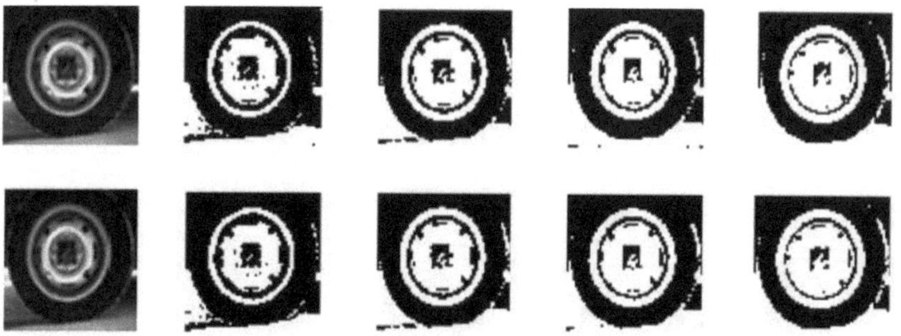

(a) Original image (b) N=1, $H(P)$=0.90 (c) N=4, $H(P)$=0.96 (d) N=5, $H(P)$=0.97 (e) N=7, $H(P)$=0.99

Fig. 9.33. Results of Tire with manually initialized threshold ($T_0 = 60$)

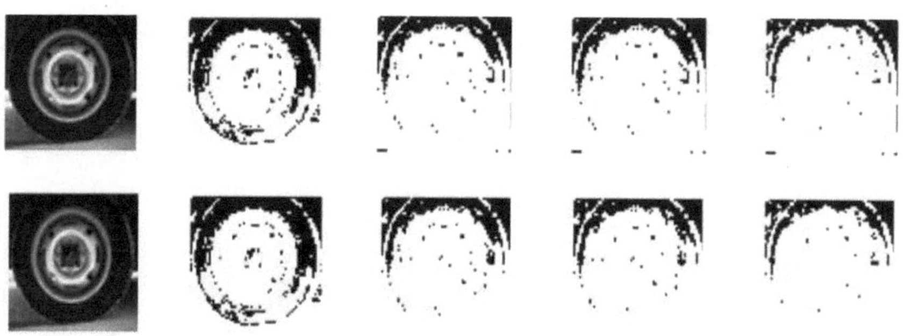

(a) Original image (b) N=1, $H(P)$=0.92 (c) N=4, $H(P)$=0.76 (d) N=5, $H(P)$=0.73 (e) N=6, $H(P)$=0.70

Fig. 9.34. Results of Tire images with automatically initialized threshold ($T_0 = 10$)

it can be seen clearly that they are not the best segmented results, because the details of Cell and Tire were not segmented clearly at this moment. The best segmented results are shown in Fig. 9.29(b) and Fig. 9.33(b), respectively, and their thresholds are set manually.

The module diagram of PCNN system based on the FPGA is shown

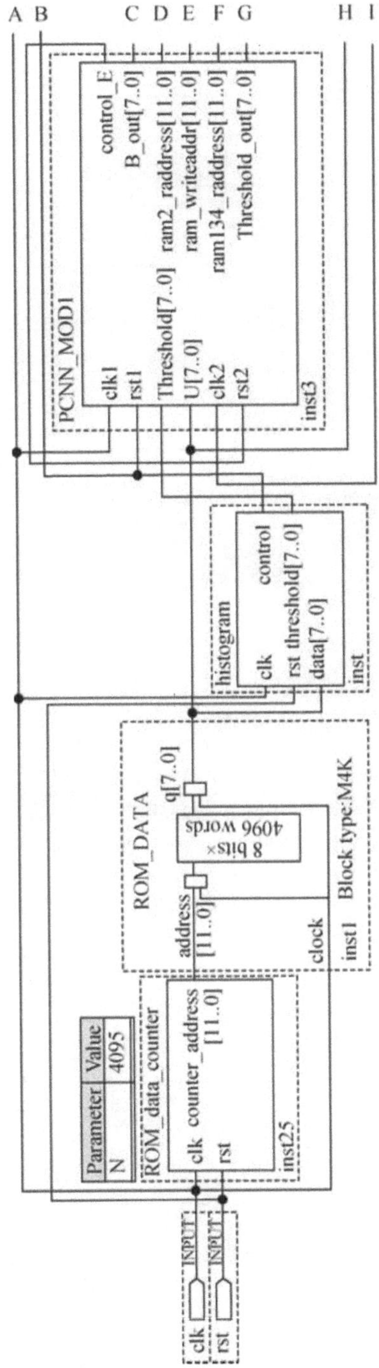

Fig. 9.35. Implementation of PCNN algorithm on FPGA (EP2C70F896C6)(part 1)

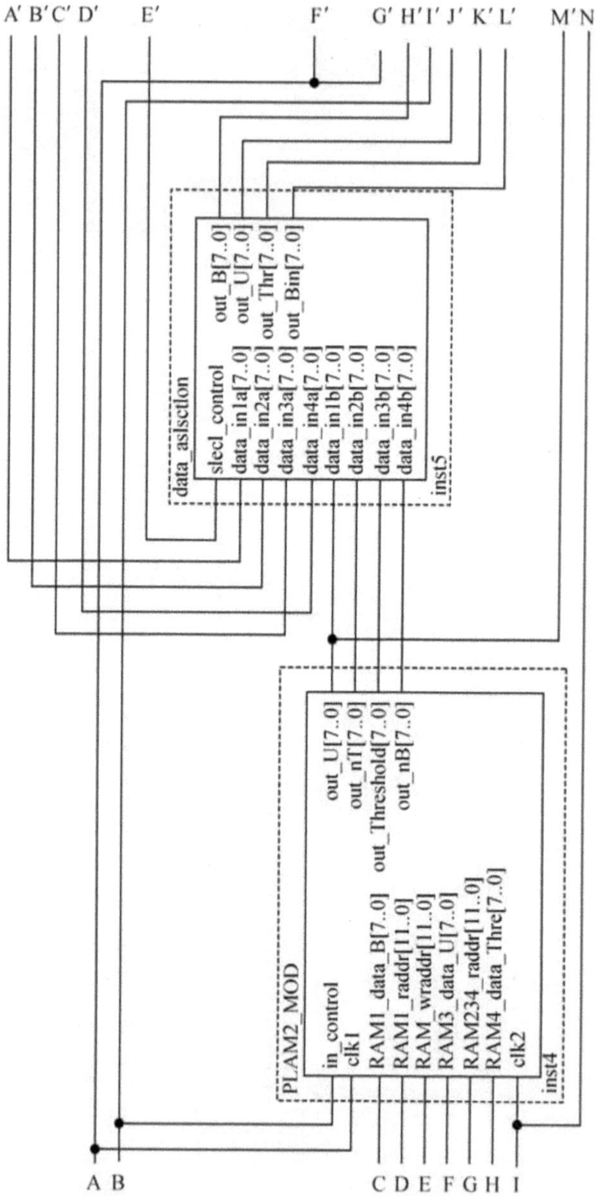

Fig. 9.36. Implementation of PCNN algorithm on FPGA (EP2C70F896C6)(part 2)

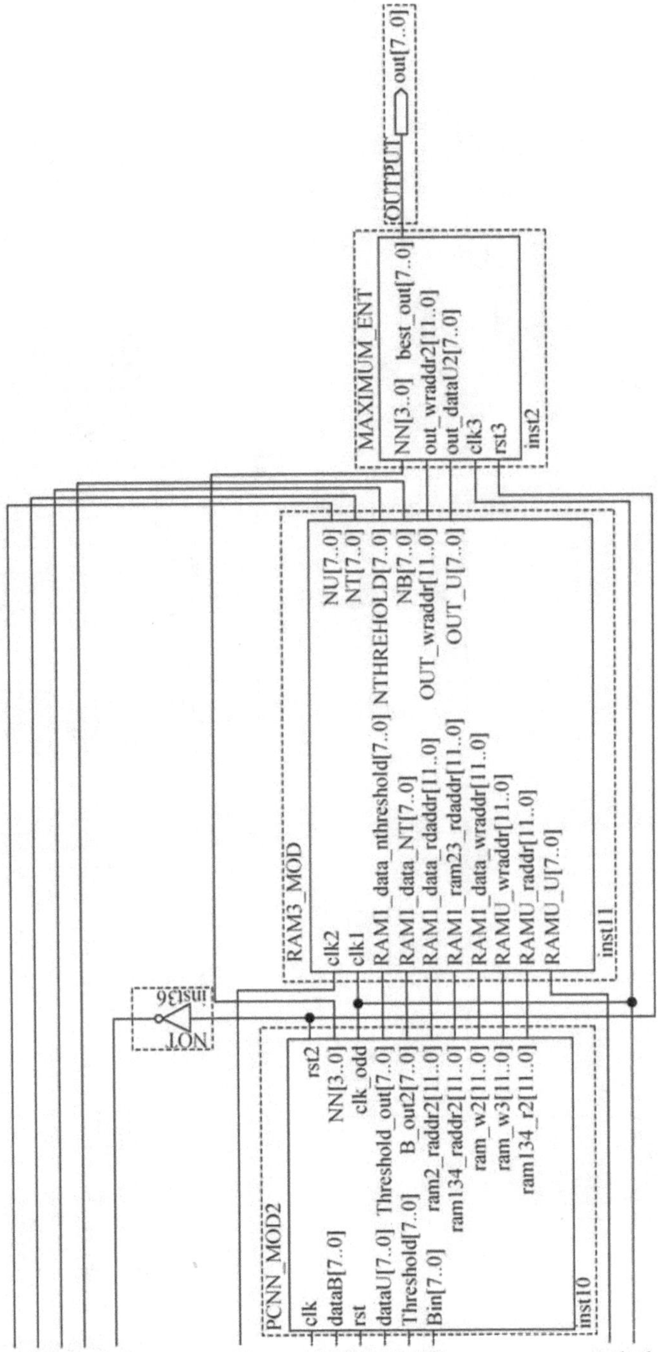

Fig. 9.37. Implementation of PCNN algorithm on FPGA (EP2C70F896C6) (part 3)

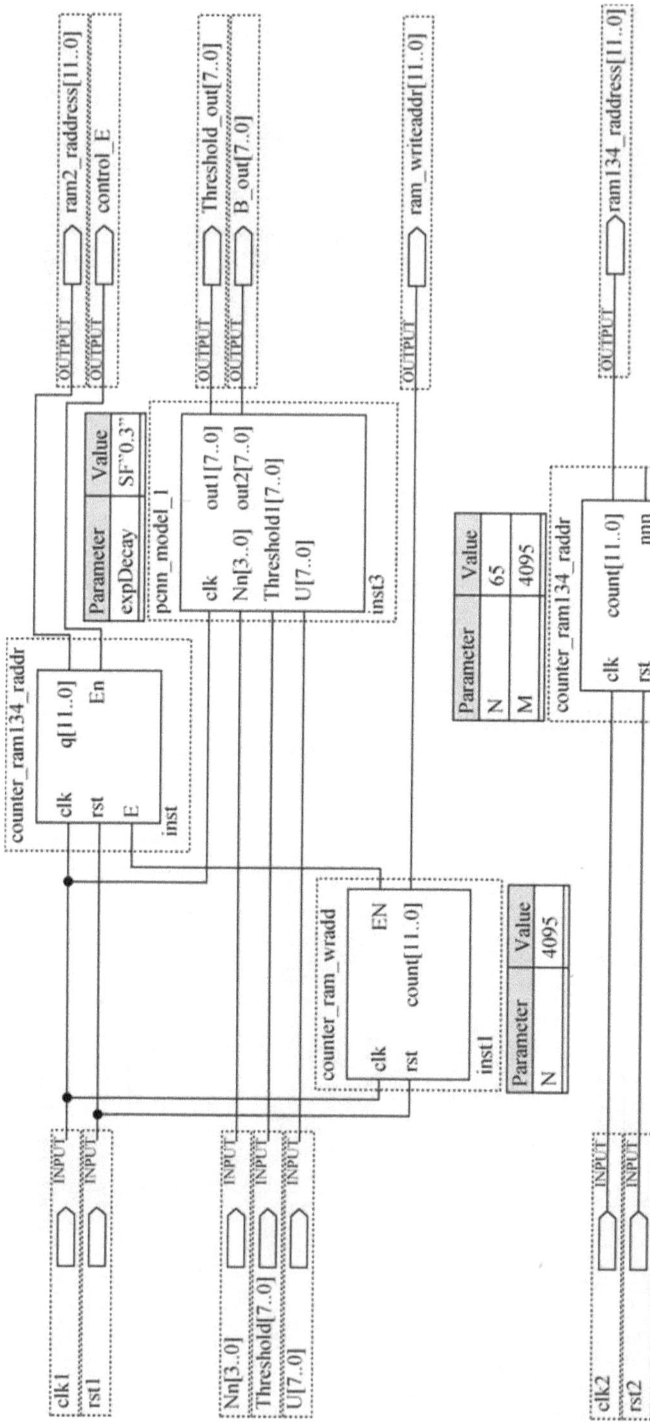

Fig. 9.38. The main logical blocks of PCNN MOD1

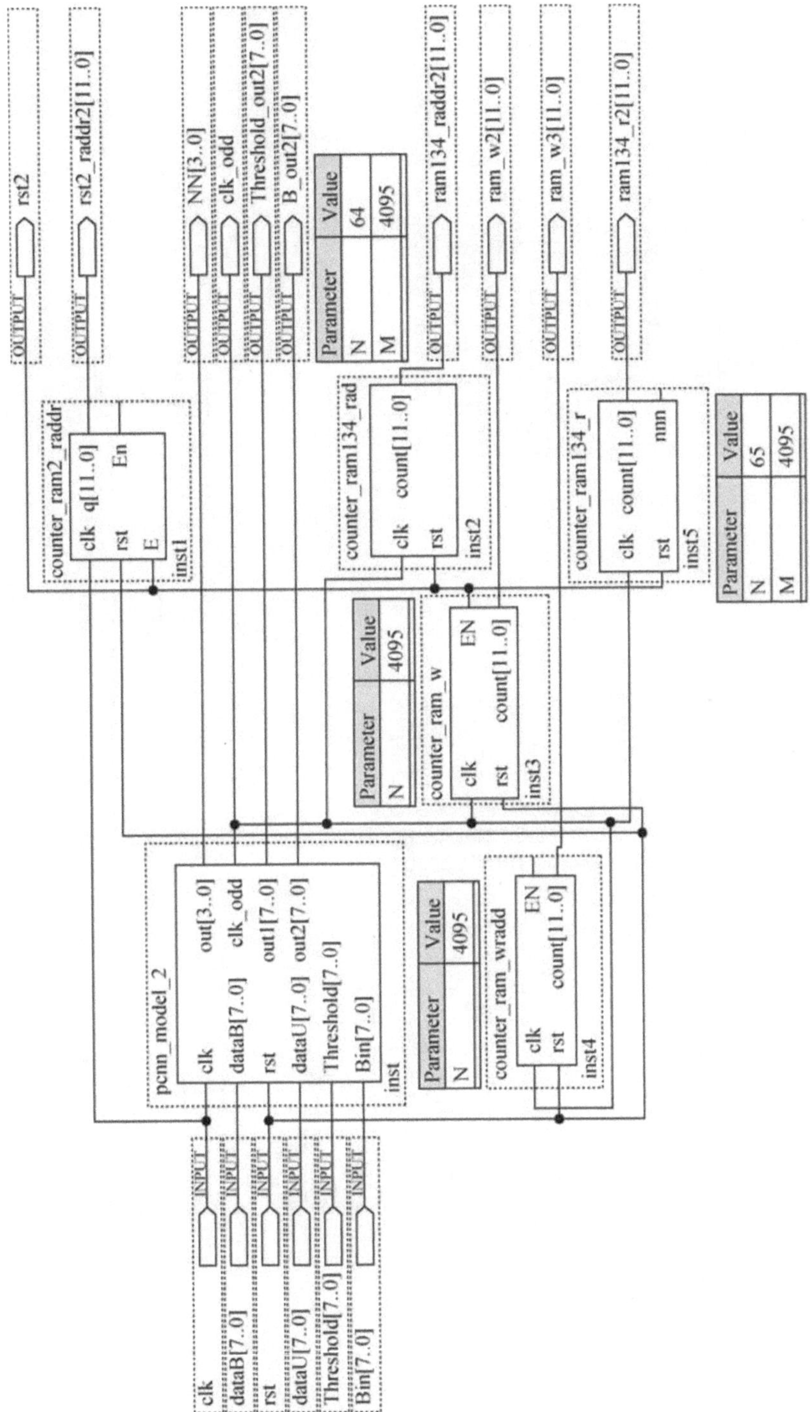

Fig. 9.39. The main logical blocks of PCNN MOD2

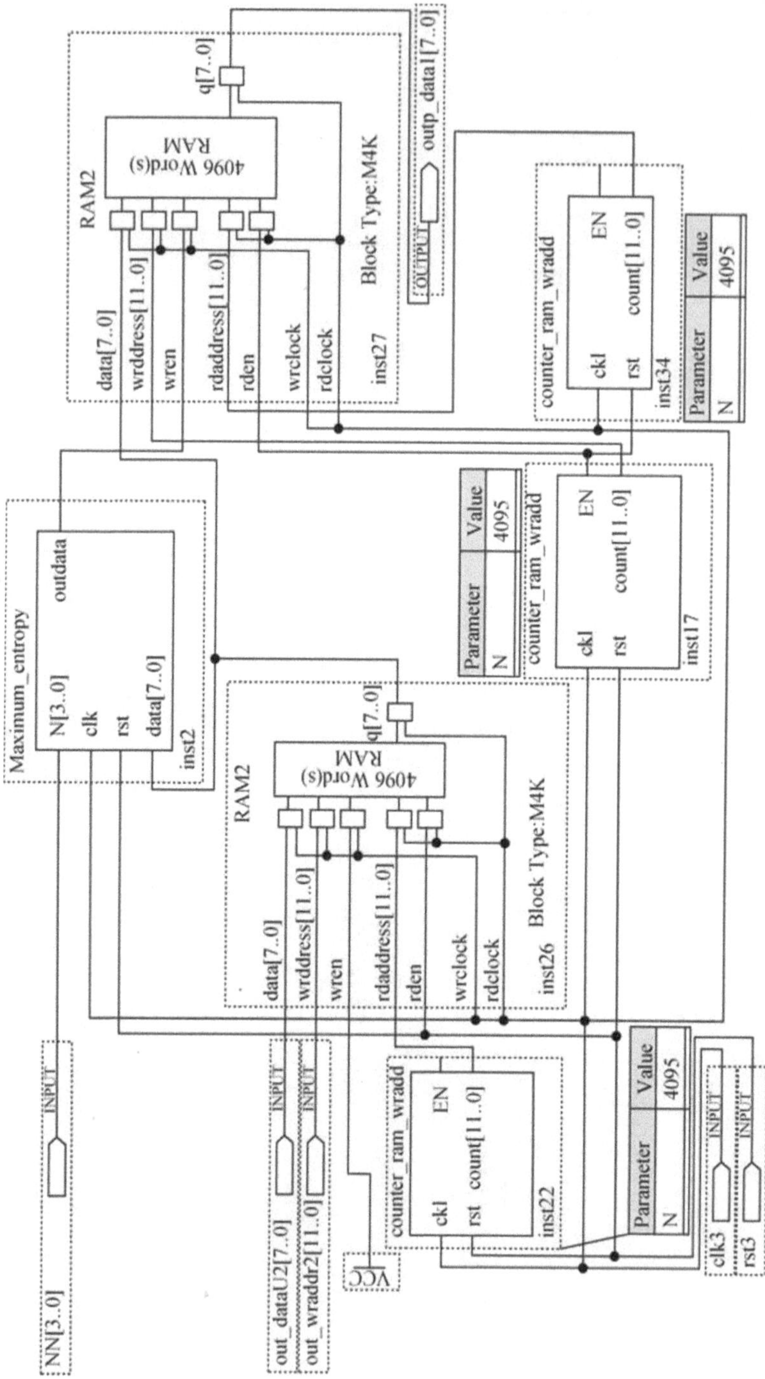

Fig. 9.40. The main logical blocks of MAXIMUX_ENT

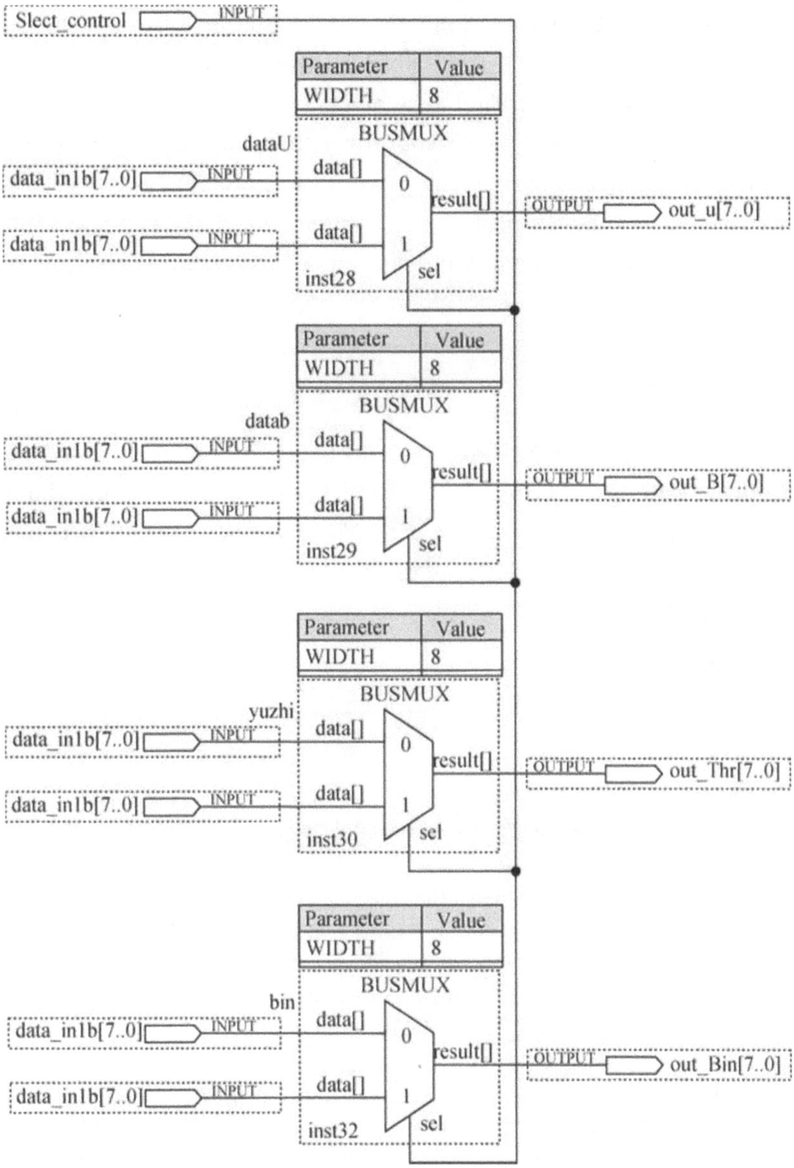

Fig. 9.41. The main logical blocks of data selection module

in Fig. 9.4. Its hardware system is composed of 3 parts, as shown in Figs. 9.35 – 9.37, respectively. Meanwhile, its PCNN_MOD1, RAM2_MOD, Data selection module and MAXIMUX_ENT module are as shown in Figs. 9.38 – 9.41, respectively.

In a word, the algorithm implemented on Altera DE2-70 can process images that have the similar characteristics of the first two group images. However, it is seen from the results of last group images that some limitations also exist in this algorithm. The one is that for some images threshold initialization module cannot generate proper threshold. The other is that using the maximum entropy rule only obtains the statistically optimal results. Hence, sometimes the segmented result cannot meet the demand of image segmentation. These problems will be discussed in the future work.

Summary

This algorithm of the PCNN was implemented on Altera DE2-70. It means a pulse image can be got faster than software simulation. Recycling the dual-port RAM and the PCNN module not only saves the hardware resources in Altera DE2-70 but also achieves an extensive use of the logic unit and RAM resources of EP2C70F896C6.

References

[1] Waldemark J, Becanovic V, Lindblad T, Lindsey CS (1997) Hybrid Neural Networks for Automatic Target Recognition. In: IEEE International Conference on Systems, Man, and Cybernetics , Orlando, 12 – 15 October 1997

[2] Larsson M, Holmstr?m Ch (1997) A study of Pulse Coupled Neural Networks for Feature extraction in Classifying Aurora Borealis. Diploma work, Department of Computer Science, Umea University, Sweden

[3] Chua LO, Yang L (1988) Cellular Neural Networks: Theory. IEEE Transactions on Circuits and Systems 35(10): 1257 – 1272

[4] Kinget P, Steyaert MSJ (1995) A programmable analog cellular neural network CMOS chip for high speed image processing. IEEE Journal of Solid-State Circuits 30(3): 235 – 243

[5] Becanovic V (1996) Diploma Work, KTH, Stockholm, TRITA-FYS-9041, 96: 9041

[6] Wilamowski BM, Jaeger RC, Padgett ML, and Myers LJ (1996) CMOS implementation of a pulse-coupled neuron cell. In: IEEE International Conference on Neural Networks, Washington, 3 – 6 June 1996

[7] Ota Y, Wilamowski BM (1999) Analog Implementation of Pulse-Coupled Neural Networks. IEEE Transactions on Neural Networks 10(3): 539 – 544

[8] Chacon MMI, Zimmerman SA, Sanchez AD (2002) A pulse-coupled neural network processor. The 2002 International Joint Conference on Neural

Networks 2: 1581 – 1584

[9] Kinser JM, Lindblad Th (1999) Implementation of the Pulse-Coupled Neural Network in a CNAPS environment. IEEE Transactions on Neural Networks 10(3): 591 – 599

[10] Lindblad T, Kinser JM (1998) Image Processing Using Pulse Coupled Neural Networks. Springer, London 146 – 151

[11] Ota, Y (2002) VLSI structure for static image processing with pulse-coupled neural network. In: IEEE 28th Annual Conference of Industrial Electronics Society, Sevilla, 5 – 8 November 2002

[12] Matolin D, Schreiter J, Schiiffny R et al. (2004) Simulation and implementation of an analog VLSI pulse-coupled neural network for image segmentation. In: The 47th IEEE International Midwest Symposium on Circuits and Systems, Hiroshim, 25 – 28 July 2004

[13] Gust C (1965) Work presented at the PCNN International Workshop. University of California at San Diego. MICOM, Huntsville

[14] Swain MJ, Ballard D (1991) Color indexing. International Journal of Computer Vision 7(1): 11 – 32

[15] Forchheimer R, Ingelhag P, Jansson C (1992) MAPP2200: A second generation smart optical sensor. In Proceedings of SPIE, Image Processing, and Interchange, 1659: 2 – 11

[16] Waldemark J, Lindblad T, Millberg M et al. (2000) Implementation of a pulse coupled neural network in FPGA. International Journal of Neural Systems 10(3): 171 – 177

[17] Millberg M, ?berg J, Waldemark J, et al. (1998) Generic VHDL Implementation of a PCNN with Loadable Coefficients. Proceedings of SPIE 3728: 186 – 197

[18] Vega-Pineda J, Chacon-M I, Camarillo-Cisneros R (2006) Synthesis of pulse-coupled neural networks in FPGAS for real-time image segmentation. In: IEEE International Joint Conference on Neural Networks, Vancouver, 16 – 21 July 2006

[19] Wang X, Ma YD (2010), Implementation of PCNN image segmentation with the maximum entropy rule on FPGA of Altera DEC-2. IEEE Transactions on Circuits and Systems (under review).

[20] Ma YD, Dai R L, Li L (2001) A new algorithm of image segmentation based on pulse-coupled neural networks and the entropy of images. In: The 8th International Conference on Neural Information Processing Shanghai, 14 – 18 November 2001.

Index

SPRINGER NATURE

GPSR Compliance

The European Union's (EU) General Product Safety Regulation (GPSR) is a set of rules that requires consumer products to be safe and our obligations to ensure this.

If you have any concerns about our products, you can contact us on ProductSafety@springernature.com

In case Publisher is established outside the EU, the EU authorized representative is:

Springer Nature Customer Service Center GmbH
Europaplatz 3
69115 Heidelberg, Germany

FSC
www.fsc.org
MIX
Papier | Fördert
gute Waldnutzung
FSC® C083411

Kolibri 360 GmbH
Ferdinand-Jühlke-Straße 7
99095 Erfurt, Deutschland
produktsicherheit@kolibri360.de